LEGO® EV3 ROBOTICS:
A Guide for Educators

Mariappan Jawaharlal

Professor of Mechanical Engineering
California State Polytechnic University, Pomona

Lego® EV3 Robotics: A Guide for Educators
Copyright © 2016 by Mariappan Jawaharlal

ISBN-13: 978-0-9983328-0-2
ISBN-10: 0-9983328-0-1

Publisher: Red Gerbera
Cover and Interior: M Subramanian
MyBot Photos: Jiapeng He
Task Pictures: Lorenzo Gutierrez
Copyediting: Todd Larsen

First Published: November 2013

Library of Congress Control Number
2016958411

LEGO® is a trademark of the LEGO® Group of companies.

Contents

Acknowledgments

First, I wish to thank Dr. Cordelia Ontiveros, Dean of the College of Engineering at California State Polytechnic University, Pomona, who has been a rock-solid supporter of Robot Rally since its inception.

I would also like to thank Dr. Mahyar Amouzegar and Dr. Edward Hohmann, both former deans of the College of Engineering, for their staunch support of the Robot Rally program during their tenure.

I am grateful to my wife, Rita, for accompanying me on my travels to many schools in Los Angeles, China and India to help me teach robotics, and to my daughters, Melissa and Lavanya, who unknowingly became my test objects a long time ago. I am excited that they have taken robotics way beyond my imagination: they not only completed undergraduate engineering degrees, but also went on to start a STEM education company that was featured on *Shark Tank*.

I want to thank the hundreds of teachers and principals over the years who have been part of this program and helped it to reach thousands of students. Special thanks go to Rosa Mendieta, Kerri Applegate, Sarah Opakiewicz, Ernesto DeSantiago, Shelley Andros, Janet Romo, and Ray Dunlap for being the early adopters of this program and enthusiastic supporters of it.

Background

The introduction of the Lego® RCX system in 1998 was a great leap forward in bringing robotics education into K-12 classrooms. It excited me about the prospect of using robotics in elementary schools. From RCX to NXT to EV3, much has changed in robotics education the last 18 years.

I initially bought a few RCX kits and started to work on them with my daughters, who were in elementary school then. Within a few days, they had built all of the models in the book, including the difficult ones, started to program the robots, and even started to create their own designs. From that moment on, I knew we could use robotics education to inspire young students. When I approached a few schools to volunteer to teach robotics, I was hoping to get an enthusiastic response. To my surprise, I never heard back from them. It was apparently too early to introduce robotics to the classroom as part of its regular curriculum.

So we began our robotics education initiative in 2003 in an afterschool program in Pomona, California, working with elementary student using Lego® and high-school students on FIRST robotics for two years. Then we started our first formal in-school program at a local elementary school with about 25 students, meeting with them once a week for about 12 weeks. I taught the first class myself, and at the end of the year we wanted to do something unique. So we brought the students to California State Polytechnic University, Pomona, for an annual event at which students displayed their creations and participated in sumo robot and obstacle course challenges. We called the event Robot Rally, where students would display their skills rather than compete. Since then, the program has been growing. We are reaching more and more schools and students every year.

Now we are using Cal Poly Pomona's largest available facility (our gym) to host the event. On May 6, 2016, we had our 10th Annual Robot Rally, which more than 1,000 students attended. We now call it Robotics Education Through Active Learning (REAL). Below is some historical information about the REAL program:

- REAL has grown from a small afterschool program of ten students in 2003 to 1,000+ students from 20 schools and an after-school program involving eight school districts each year.

- Its primary focus is on elementary school students.

- Cal Poly Pomona Engineering students visit local schools, support teachers and mentor students.

- Cal Poly Pomona Engineering faculty train teachers and visit classrooms.

- So far, more than 8,000 students have gone through the program, including after-school programs.

- More than 200 undergraduate students have participated in the program.

- More than 400 teachers trained in the program

- More than 75% of our students come from low-income families.

- About 51% of REAL participants are girls.

- All participants expressed interest in a STEM career after completing REAL.

- REAL is the largest program of its kind in the nation.

Why This Book?

The challenge we faced from our early days of robotics education was the lack of a structured curriculum guide teachers can use. There are numerous books on Lego® Robotics, but they mostly show different robots and give instructions on how to build them. Our goal is to provide teachers a structured approach to teaching robotics in order to help students to have an engaging learning experience. Our teachers come from very diverse educational backgrounds: mathematics, physics, English, history, and even physical education. Since most students in the REAL program gather for its annual Robot Rally, we want to make sure they all go through comparable learning experiences. So consistency is key, and this guide addresses that need.

The best way to begin robotics is to build and program the robots. We recommend any teacher or parent who is interested in teaching robotics to go through this guide and follow the instructions to build and program the robot. Instructions for an easy-to-build robot, MyBot, are included. I hope the guide also provides just enough information without overwhelming the reader. It also provides tips for classroom management and interaction with students.

My main suggestion for teachers and parents is: Give just enough information, and let your students figure out the rest. Ask them, "What do you think?" every time they ask a question. Don't answer it right away unless the student has apparently spent a lot of time on the question already and is frustrated. Even in this scenario, I give them just enough information for them to overcome their frustration.

In addition, unless you are a geek yourself and willing to spend a lot of time doing robotics, my advice is to acknowledge that many of your students will learn robotics faster than you have one, and will know more about the subject than you do soon. This experience may be new for you. Embrace it. This is exactly what you want from your students. If you see some of your students marching ahead of you, ask them to become your helpers. Give them additional responsibilities and more challenging tasks for that purpose.

This guide is designed for educators working with elementary and middle school students. It is a curriculum plan for teachers, not a comprehensive guide for EV3 programming. It does not deal with advanced functionalities, but it provides a strong foundation to build on with examples that have been tested and used thousands of times.

This book is divided into units. Depending upon how much class time is available, you can do one or more units in each session.

We have designed this teachers' guide to be accessible to all. I hope you will find it useful in your robotics education initiatives.

—Mariappan Jawaharlal, Ph.D.
Professor
California State Polytechnic University, Pomona

Why Teach Robotics?

Robotics is increasingly becoming the fourth "R" of learning—after "Reading, wRriting and aRithmetic"—that modern-day students must understand in order to succeed in a highly competitive, technology-driven world. Robotics integrates all STEM fields in way no other subject can. In that sense, Robotics is the intersection of many disciplines, as it integrates mechanics, electronics, electrical and control engineering, computer science, technology, math and science. You will discover breakthrough technologies in Robotics. Immerse yourself in the most forward-looking discipline of our time. Robotics:

- Makes learning fun, engaging, and inspiring;
- Provides highly practical hands-on experience;
- Gives students a head start in preparing for high school and college;
- Develops critical thinking skills and problem-solving strategies;
- Enables students to develop and express creativity;
- Develops the ability to work collaboratively in teams;
- Helps students to develop an intuitive understanding of physical concepts in science and math, to excel in those fields, and to consider careers in science and technology;
- Enables the learner to appreciate and realize technology;
- Builds confidence and self-esteem in the learner;
- Prepares the learner for the fast-paced competitive world

What Do We Need?

Hardware

- Lego® Education EV3 basic kit (can be purchased only from Lego® Education in the US)
- PC or Mac (one computer for each student or each 3-member student team)
- Computer-screen projector

Software

- Lego® EV3 software

Material and Supplies

- Engineer's notebook
- Mission mats or tapes (blue tape or multi-colored duct tapes) for creating missions
- Color mats for color recognition and obstacle-course missions
- Sumo ring (4 ft. ideally, 3 ft. minimum), a diameter ring painted black or white inside with 1 in. white or black border
- Rulers/tape measures
- Zip ties/rubber bands

Classroom organization

- Install EV3 software on each computer. One computer per team is desirable.
- A table for each team is preferable. Ideally, each team should have no more than 3 members.

- Locate the computers and tables to allow enough open space for activity in the classroom.

Introduce Ground Rules

Explain the importance of ground rules to the students. Ask students why it is important to follow rules in their favorite games, such as basketball or soccer. Your students will probably tell you they need rules for safety, consistency and fairness. Let them know for the same reason, in order to make the experience meaningful, that we have certain ground rules and will enforce them collectively.

Rules about preparation, material handling and clean-up

- How to keep the lid at the bottom and the box on top so it is stable.
- Take care of your kit. Don't lose small parts. If you do, you won't be able to complete your robot!
- How to organize the parts in the various compartments of the plastic bin.
- Don't use your teeth to take parts apart: you may break your teeth, and it is unhygienic. If you have difficulty taking out a pin, use an axle push it out.
- No horseplay or throwing anything.
- No food, drinks or gum allowed in the classroom.
- No whining allowed.

Teamwork

- A student who has a question must check with his team first. If they cannot be of help, the student must ask another team member from the next table. If no one can help with the questions, then the student can ask the teacher.
- How do we collaborate? Discuss ways students can help each other, and the importance of working together, including the ways teamwork is the key to success in various sports.

Using the Engineer's Notebook

- Discuss the importance of writing down one's ideas, observations, experimental results and collected data, as well as drawing sketches. Let them know that this is what creative people do. Let them know that they have complete freedom to whatever they want. If possible, show an example of Engineer's Notebook. This is not a lecture class. Do not force them to write anything. Most students will start to use the notebook at some point in time.

- Encourage students to take notes on their own and write down what they think is important.

- Encourage them to draw sketches of what they observe.

- Encourage them to write a summary of what they have done at the end of the day. You must allow a few minutes at the end of each session for them to gather their thoughts.

1

Introduction to Robotics and Engineering Terms

STUDENT LEARNING OUTCOMES

- To articulate what a robot is and name the important parts of a robotic system.
- To name and describe the main building components in the kit.

What is a robot?

Interestingly, a robot has no standard definition. For many, a robot may recall humanlike creatures (androids, monsters, etc.) seen in many movies. However, millions of robots are now used in the industry, and even in our homes, that do not resemble human beings at all.

Ask your students: What is a robot? Let them come up with their own answers; there are no wrong ones here. Every answer can be tied to robotics in some way, and you should encourage that. Help your students to brainstorm to come up with terms that define a robot in their mind. Write down key terms on the board. Prompt students with familiar examples, such as the Roomba vacuum cleaner, the Mars Rover, and robots in movies such as *I, Robot* and *Star Wars.*

So, instead of defining robots, list a robot's essential features. Compare humans with robots and list their common attributes: body (structure), motion (motors), five senses (sensors), brain (controller/computer).

Major parts of a robot

Structure: Robots have internal structures, as we have skeletons.

Sensors: Robots have sensors, as we have abilities to see, hear and touch.

Actuators: Robots have motors for movement, as we have the ability to move.

Computer: Robots need a processor, like our brains.

Software: Robots need to control algorithms to make decisions, as our brain enables us to think.

Power: Robots need power, as we need food and liquid for energy.

The importance of learning the correct engineering terminology

Emphasize why we want to use correct engineering terms, and the importance of doing so. Engineers use specific words to mean specific things, which avoids ambiguity and misunderstanding. This type of communication is also key to becoming a professional engineer. So students must avoid such vague, colloquial terms as "give me that *thingie*." Encourage students to write down or sketch names of particular robot parts in their notebooks.

Introduce students to various parts in the kit. This entire process will take about 20-30 minutes. Don't lecture about parts; hold a part up so students can clearly see it, ask them to select that part from their kit, state its name, and write down the name on the board in clear block letters. Provide real-world applications of each part discussed.

1. **Structural Elements:**

    a. **Beam**

      - A beam is a structural component used to support a structure.

      - How to differentiate between different-sized beams? Instead of giving answers, pose the question and see if someone can figure it out. *Answer:* Count the number of holes in a beam: three holes in a Size 3 beam, five holes in a Size 5 beam, etc.

      - The uses of beams in the real world: Beams are used to build structures, but not only in buildings. Cars, airplanes and ships have internal structures, and beams are used to create them. Even the bones in a human body's internal skeletal structure are beams.

b. **Axle**

- An axle is a slender rod that allows the transfer of rotational motion from one part to another.
- The types of axles we use in our robot kit are really called shafts. We will use those terms interchangeably in this course, although there is a difference between them, which we will not worry about for now.
- Shafts connect motors to wheels.
- How to differentiate between different-sized axles? Hold an axle next to a beam, pose that question, and see if someone can figure out. *Answer:* An axle's length can be specified by comparing the length to the number of holes in a beam: Size 3 axle, Size 7 beam, etc.
- The use of axles in the real world: Axles and shafts support gears, wheels and pulleys.

c. **Pin**

- Pin types: Friction pin (black color), smooth pin (gray color), double pin, axle pin.
- Pins connect two beams, allowing rotation between them. To create rotational motion between beams, use a smooth pin. With a friction pin, rotation will be tight; it will be a lot easier with a smooth pin. Demonstrate this to students, and ask them to try out.
- If you use two pins between two beams, it becomes a structure.
- A double pin connects three beams together.
- An axle pin is an axle one side and a pin on the other side.
- The use of pins in real world: Pins in door hinges, a pin holding the two parts of a scissor, etc.

d. **Bushing**

- Bushings come in two sizes: half-bushing (half the size of full bushing) and full bushing, which is simply called a bushing.
- Bushings are used with axles.
- The use of bushings in the real world: Bushings are used to support shafts to reduce friction. We will use bushings s spacers.

e. **Gears**

- A gear is a toothed wheel that works with another gear to increase or decrease the speed.

- Gears are used to transfer rotational motion from one shaft (axle) to another.

- Gears come in various sizes. They can be differentiated by the number of teeth they have.

- The use of gears in the real world: Gears are used in automobile transmissions.

f. **Various other parts**

- L-Beams, bent beams, etc. You can be creative and make up your own name for a beam with a different or unusual shape or formation.

- Pulley, or block-and-tackle.

g. **Connectors**

- Axle joiners – used to join two axles together into one long axle unit.

- Connectors – There are numerous connectors in the kit. Identify and learn to use them when needed. Example: an angle connector will allow you to connect two beams at 90°.

h. **Other parts**

- This kit has many more elements that can be used to create a complex robot model. It is enough for students to learn the names of key elements discussed above. Help students to start using the terms. At the end of the course, they will be talking like professional engineers.

2. End this lesson with a quick review of all parts. Hold up each of the following pieces and ask the class to state its name. Then have a student to volunteer the real-world application of that part.

a. Beam
b. Axle
c. Pin
d. Double Pin
e. Bushing
f. Half-bushing
g. Gear

2

Introduction to Sensors, Motors and the EV3 brick

STUDENT LEARNING OUTCOMES

- To recall engineering terms from the previous session;
- To identify sensors and describe their functionality and how to use them;
- To operate the EV3 brick: switching it on and off, charging it, navigating it through menus and using its buttons.
- To operate motors with the EV3 brick.

Introduce Sensors

Ask students: What are the five senses of the human body?

a. Sight
b. Touch
c. Hearing
d. Smell
e. Taste

Our robot kit has its own sensors. While our sensors are very unique and work differently, we can still make some comparisons with robot sensors.

Sight: This can be obtained in a robot by combining an ultrasonic sensor with a color sensor.

Ultrasonic Sensor: This generates high frequency sound waves we cannot hear and measures the time in which the echo is received. It uses ultrasonic waves, similar to those of bats, dolphins and whales.

Color Sensor: This enables us to differentiate colors. LEGO® color sensors can distinguish six colors.

Touch Sensor: This detects the push and release. It is also called a bump sensor. We can correlate our touch-sensing ability to the touch sensor.

Hearing: We can correlate our hearing ability to a sound sensor. However, our robot kit has no sound sensors. It can be purchased separately.

Smell: Our robot kit has no smell sensor.

Taste: Our robot kit has no taste sensor.

Gyroscopic sensor: We use this to measure angular velocity. The LEGO® gyro sensor measures the robot's rotational motion and changes its orientation. This sensor is useful for determining the change in the angle in a specific plane. We can use this sensor to create balancing vehicles, such as Segway.

Introduce the Brick

- The brick is like the brain of our robot: it has four **input** and four **output** ports.
- Input ports enable the sensors to receive information from the robot's environment. For example, when the ultrasonic sensor picks up an object ahead, the sensor sends distance information to the brick.
- Output ports are for the motors.
- A port on the brick connects the brick to the computer.
- Ports for a USB and an SD card are also on the brick.
- Walk the students through the process of navigating the EV3. By the end of this exercise, students should be proficient in turning the brick on and off and navigating through its various menu options.

EV3 Brick Buttons

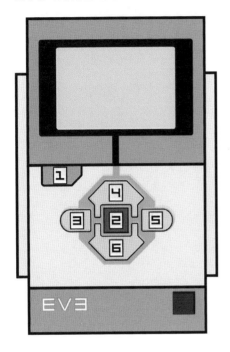

1. **Back button:** Allows the user to go back to a previous step, to abort a program, or to shut down the brick.

2. **Enter button:** Acts like the 'Enter' button on a computer; used for selecting desired options.

3. **Move the cursor to the left.** Used to move through the content displayed on the screen.

4. **Move the cursor up.** Used to move or scroll through the content displayed on the screen.

5. **Move the cursor to the right.** Used to move through the content displayed on the screen.

6. **Move the cursor down.** Used to move or scroll through the content displayed on the screen.

EV3 Top Menu

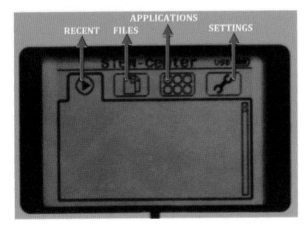

1. **Recent:** Shows the most recent programs downloaded to the brick.

2. **Files:** Manages files stored on the EV3 as well as on the SD card.

3. **Brick applications:** Includes port view, motor control, IR control, and brick data log.

4. **Settings:** Changes various settings on the brick.

Introduce the Motors

- Our robot can use up to 4 motors.

- Motors are connected to output ports. Why are they called output ports? Think about the human analogy.

- Discuss what a motor is, and how it is used in the real world. For example, motors convert electrical energy into mechanical energy and transmit rotary motion. Fans, blenders, and washing machines are each connected to a motor.

Wrap-up

End this lesson by reviewing the different sensors. Hold up each sensor and ask students to name it, describe its function, and state whether it is an input port or an output port.

3

EV3 Experiments

STUDENT LEARNING OUTCOMES

- To use the color sensor, identify various colors, and measure the reflected light intensity (RLI).
- To measure distance using ultrasonic sensors.
- To use the gyro sensor, measure the angle about an axis, and reset the gyro.
- To attach the motors to output ports and control the motor.
- To explain the difference between rotations and degrees, as well as the correlation between them.

How to run the EV3 Experiments

The students will conduct these experiments. However, the instructor should give a 10-minute demonstration before the students begin. Ask students to use their notebook to record their observations.

Ultrasonic Sensor – Determine your height

1. Instruct all students to take turns. Students in each team do one experiment at a time.

2. Show them how to connect the wire to the sensor and the EV3 brick. Remind them to be gentle with the wires.

3. Instruct students to connect the ultrasonic sensor to port 4. Using right (or left) arrow key(s), move to Applications: **Applications → Select Port View → Use the right arrow key to move to port 4.** Press 'Enter' and select CM or IN.

   a. Move your hands slowly in front of the ultrasonic sensor and see how the distance value changes on the display.

   b. Ask students to guess the height of the distance values, in cm.

Give students about 10 minutes to complete this experiment. Walk around and help them. Most will figure out how to hold the sensor just at the head level while it faces the floor and how to measure the value accordingly. You can also ask students to figure out the distance to the ceiling. Common mistakes they make are to place the sensor so it does not face the floor properly, or to permit obstruction between the sensor and the floor.

Color Sensor

1. Instruct students to connect the color sensor to port 3. Using right (or left) arrow key(s), move to Applications: **Applications → Select Port View → Use the right arrow key to move to port 3**. Press enter and select RLI (you have the option to choose Ambient Light Intensity, or Color, which we will do later).

2. Put your robot down on various colored surfaces, especially on black and white ones. You can use white and black papers. Make sure your robot is even and the color sensor is giving a consistent reading. Don't install the color sensor too far away from or too close to the ground; 5 to 10 mm from the floor is a good distance.

3. Measure the RLI values of the colors shown below. Make sure you take multiple readings for each color before students record the numbers in a table in their notebooks (table shown below). After recording these values, enter the numbers 1-7 for each color in the next column.

Color	RLI Value	Code
Black		
Blue		
Green		
Yellow		
Red		
White		
Brown		

4. Now set up the EV3 to display color. (You must go back to the Port view by pressing the Back button and choose the appropriate options to select *Color.*)

5. Repeat this experiment, and watch the color code displayed by the robot. If all goes well, you will get the same results as the ones you entered in the last table.

   EV3 uses the following color code:

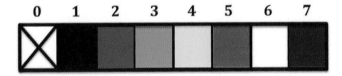

6. Set up the EV3 to measure ambient color. To measure ambient light, move the sensor away from the table. Hold it higher and slowly spin it around to see a consistent reading of ambient color.

   Enter the ambient color value: _____

Touch Sensor

1. Instruct students to connect the touch sensor to port 1. Using right (or left) arrow key(s), move to Applications: **Applications → Select Port View**

2. Press the touch sensor and see what appears on the screen. Your display must show 1 when pressed, or 0 when released. This information can be used to identify if the button is pressed or not. (We will use this function later to program the robot to see if it is touching a wall or some object.)

Gyro Sensor

1. Teach students to connect the gyro sensor to port 2. Make sure this sensor is mounted to the brick and the brick is level. Using right (or left) arrow key(s), move to Applications: **Applications → Select Port View → Use right button to move to port 2.** Press 'Enter' to select 'Angle' or 'Gyro Rate.' Choose 'Angle' for this experiment.

2. Rotate your brick slowly about a perpendicular axis and check the readings of your sensor displayed on the screen. This is the angel by which you are rotating the brick. We can use this feature to see if the robot is moving on a slope, or turn the robot by a certain angle.

Motors

1. Teach students to connect a large motor to Port B. Notice there are two large motors and one medium motor. Using right (or left) arrow key(s), move to Applications: **Applications → Select Port View → Use right button to move to port B:** Press 'Enter' to select 'Angle' or 'Rotation.' Choose Rotation for this experiment.

2. Rotate your motor B by hand and see how the display shows the number of rotations. You may find it very difficult to rotate the motor this way. To make it easier, insert an axle into the motor on one end of the axle and attach a large gear or a rim on the other.

3. Rotate the motor in the opposite direction and see what happens. Note down your observations.

4. Change the setting to 'Angle' and do the same experiment.

5. Discuss the correlation between degree and rotation.

Summary

1. Encourage students to use their notebooks or worksheets while doing these experiments. After running them, ask students to share their observations with the class. The main concepts learned from the experiments are listed below. If any are not shared during the discussion, talk about them at the end.

    a. When the touch sensor is pressed, the display shows 1. When not pressed, the screen shows 0.

b. The gyro sensor can display the how much the robot has been rotated. It can also display the rate (degrees/second) of the rotation. Make sure students understand the plane of rotation. If you are teaching middle-schoolers or a group of advanced students, you can discuss rate, which is an important concept. For example, velocity and acceleration are all rates.

c. White has a higher RLI value, while black has a lower one. Write down these numbers on the board. Keep in mind that the numbers (even for white and black) vary between teams, due to differing amounts of light on a surface, surface conditions, the way the sensor is mounted, etc.

d. The ultrasonic sensor will show 255 (in cm) or 100 (in inches) if the object is too far away from or too close to the ground to measure.

e. Both the ultrasonic sensor and the color sensor have a range. Measure the actual range.

f. The large motors (two are included in the kit) are typically

g. connected to port B and C. The medium motor (one included) should be connected to Port A. Port D is vacant and can be used with an additional motor, which can be purchased separately.

2. Encourage students to:

a. follow the instructions as written to run their EV3 experiments;

b. record all observations in their Engineer's Notebooks; and

c. ask the instructor if they have any questions.

3A

Ultrasonic Sensor – Range Estimation by Experiment (optional)

This is a fun activity that helps students to figure out the actual range of their ultrasonic sensors by experimentation, and to understand the importance of planning, designing and conducting experiments as well as and collecting and analyzing data. I encourage you to ask your students to conduct this experiment, though it can be skipped if time is limited. Yet it will be helpful for students interested taking part in competitions and for students who are looking to be further challenged.

Determine the range of ultrasonic sensor experimentally. Refer to the diagram below:

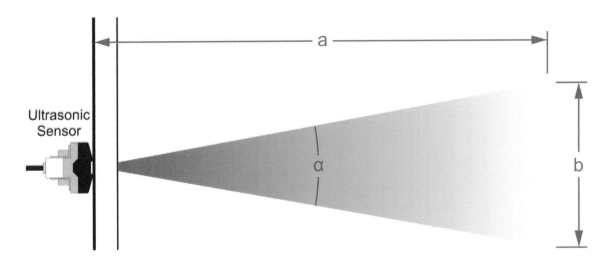

Ask students to mount the ultrasonic sensor securely on the brick or on a flat area, and then to plot the area of its influence by moving an object around it slowly. Make sure the sensor is

15

connected to the brick and you are getting readings. (You can use a piece of cardboard for this purpose.) Find the maximum and minimum distance and the angle. Take multiple readings. Write them down neatly in a table.

> **NOTE**
>
> The detectable distance is between 3 and 250 cm (accurate to +/- 1 cm). If you are using inch mode, the detectable distance is between 1 and 99 in. (with an accuracy of +/- 0.394 in.). If your sensor displays a value of 255 cm or 100 in., your sensor is not able to detect any object in front of it. This means the object is too close to or too far away from the sensor. Remember, actual measurements may vary significantly from the specified values. Write down the values in your notebook as follows:
>
> $\alpha =$ $b =$ $c =$

3B

Color Sensor – Range Estimation by Experiment (optional)

This is a fun activity that helps students to figure out the actual range of their color sensor through experiment and to understand the importance of planning, designing and conducting experiments, as well as collecting and analyzing data. I encourage you to ask your students to conduct this experiment, though it can be skipped in the regular class if time is limited. However, it will be helpful for students interested in taking part in competitions or looking to be further challenged.

The color sensor has a working range, thus works much like an ultrasonic sensor. Determine the range of the color sensor experimentally. Refer to the diagram below:

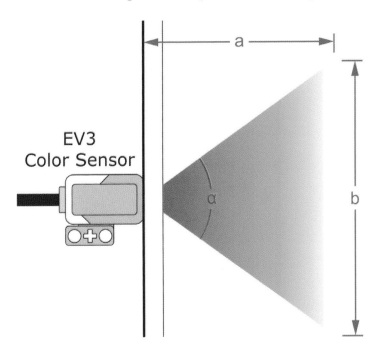

Ask students to mount the color sensor securely on the brick or on a flat area and plot the area of its influence by moving a piece of cardstock around it slowly. Make sure the sensor is connected to the brick and you are getting RLI readings. Find the maximum and minimum distance and the angle. Take multiple readings. Write them down neatly in a table as follows:

$$\alpha = \qquad\qquad b = \qquad\qquad c =$$

4

Building the MyBot

Now it is time for the students to build their MyBot. The MyBot is a compact, easy-to-build robot. It uses all major parts of the robot kit, including all three motors and four sensors.

All students must take turns building. Each student can complete two steps and then pass the robot to the next student. Students are encouraged to help each other on the steps and get pieces for their steps while waiting their turns. The instructor should walk around and make sure every student has a chance to build.

Some students may dominate the building process or say, "Let me build it fast," etc. The instructor must announce that building the MyBot is not a competition, and that making a mistake is good thing: all you have to do is take it apart and do it again. This may take some extra time but you will learn how to build the MyBot properly. If you don't make any mistakes, you will likely do so later, which is not desirable. Make mistakes now, as much as you can, but be sure to follow the MyBot instructions at the end of this section.

STUDENT LEARNING OUTCOMES

- To identify various parts and know each part's terminology and function.
- To build (assemble) the robot using various structural elements.

Steps to Building the MyBot

1. Each student should complete 1 or 2 steps.

2. Build the body of the MyBot using the step-by-step instructions below.

3. Be sure the left motor is connected to port B and the right motor is connected to port C. Both are large motors.

NOTE TO INSTRUCTORS

It is advisable to stop building after students complete the basic robot and go to the next lesson for programming. Students can then attach the touch sensor and return to programming. However, it is difficult to control the building process or make every student team build at the same speed. So you can allow the students who are building faster to complete the entire robot with sensors.

4. Attach the touch and gyro sensors.

5. Be sure the sensors are connected to the corresponding ports:

   a. Touch – 1

   b. Gyro – 2

   c. Color – 3

   d. Ultrasonic – 4

Once the students have completed the MyBot, the instructor should check to make sure it is built correctly. Things to watch for:

- A common building mistake: flipping (mirror-image) a sub-assembly on one side.
- Cables not connected or secured into the ports properly. (You will feel a click when it is secured properly.)
- Wires touching the wheels, or just dragging.
- Cables or other objects in front of the ultrasonic sensor, obstructing its view.

MYBOT BUILDING INSTRUCTIONS

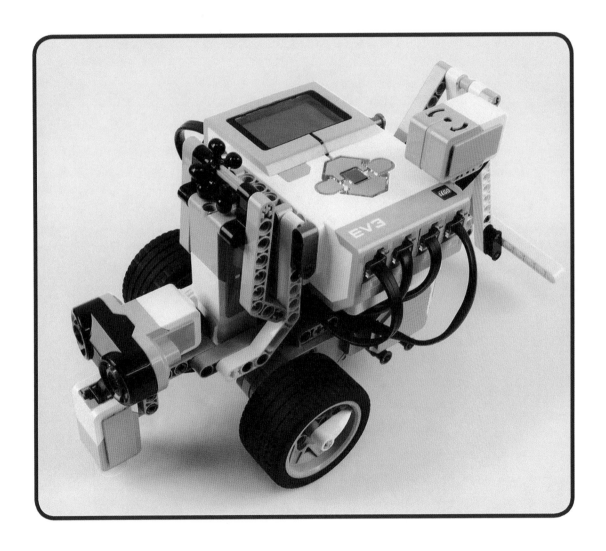

BASIC ROBOT

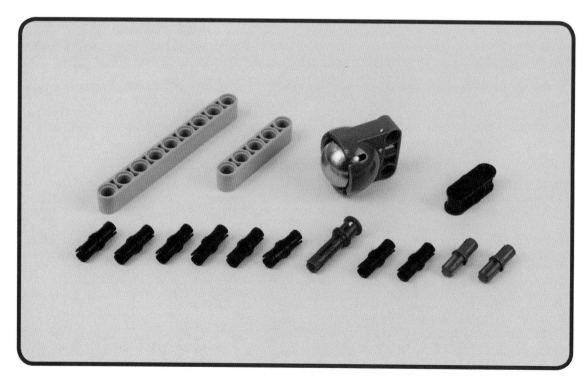

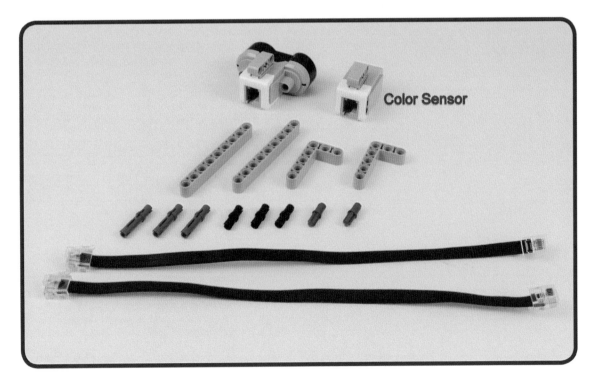

Color Sensor

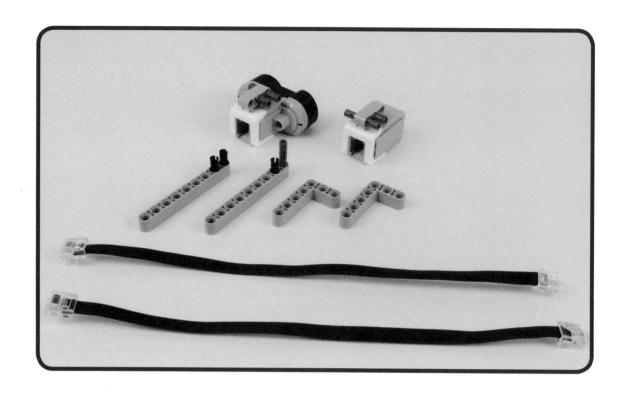

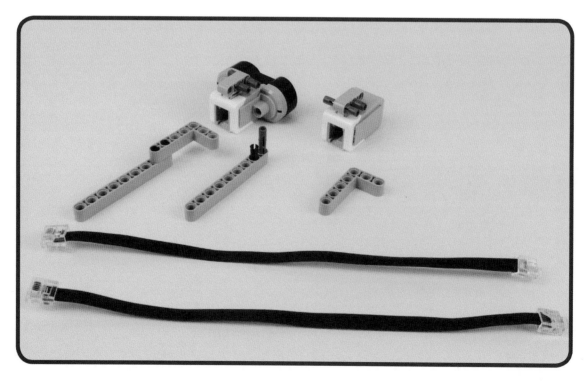

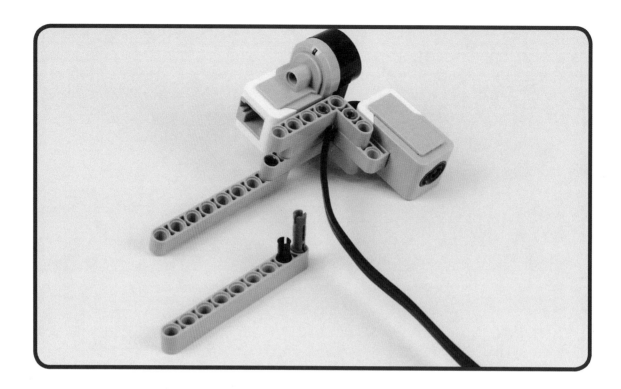

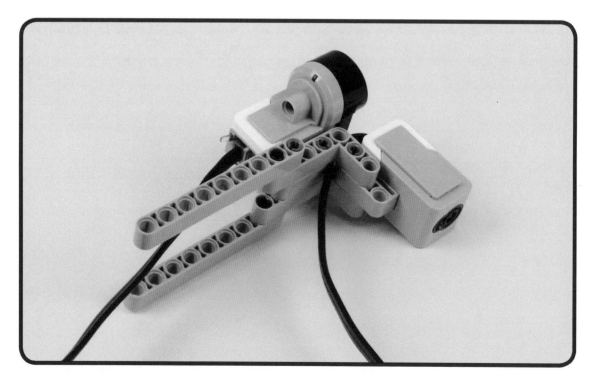

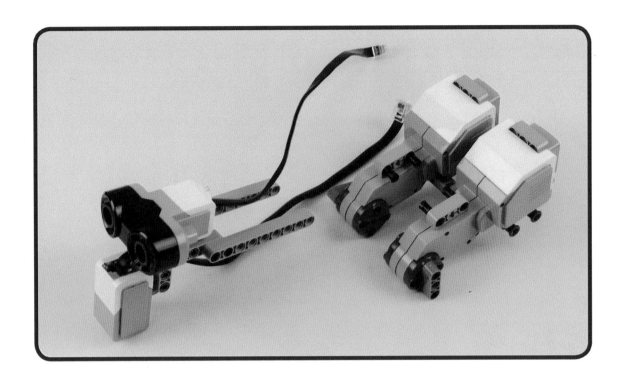

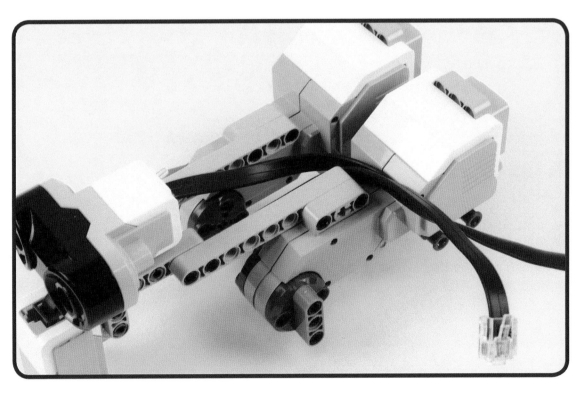

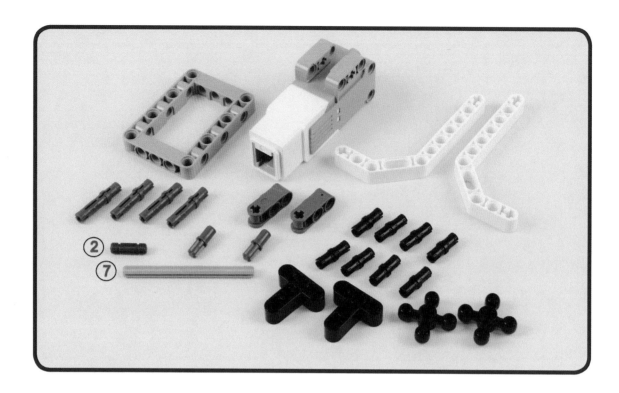

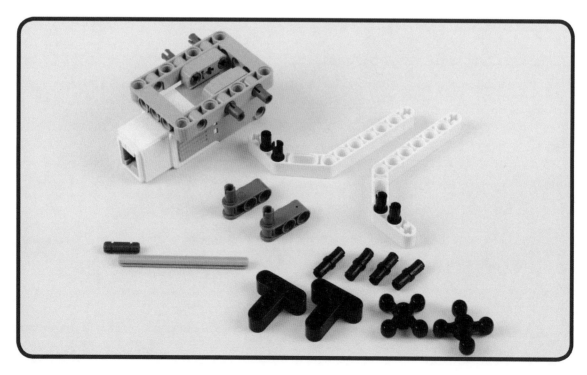

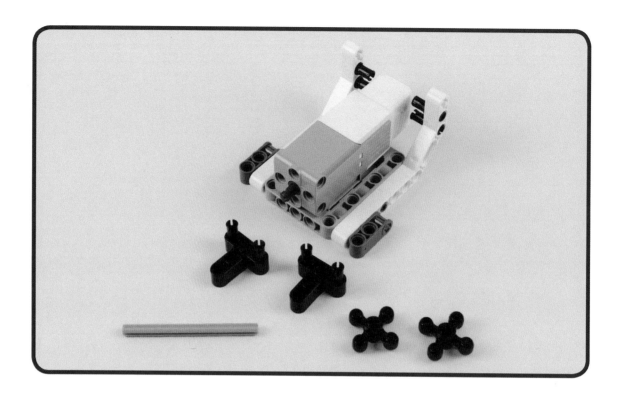

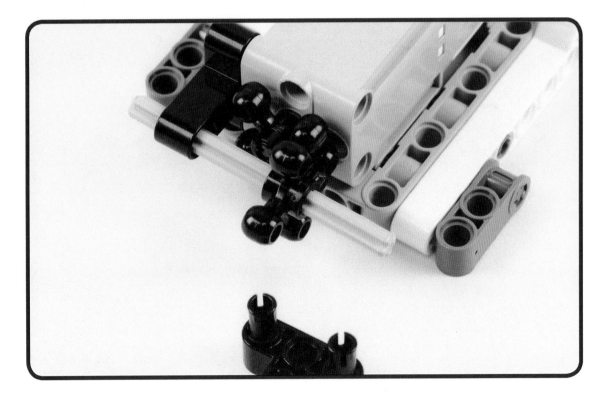

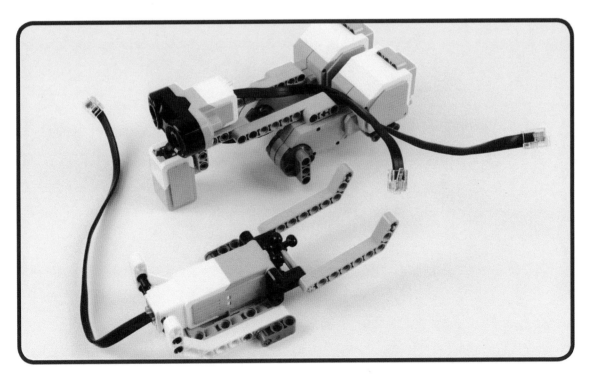

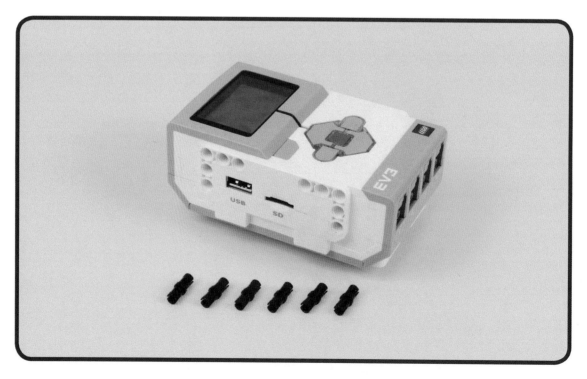

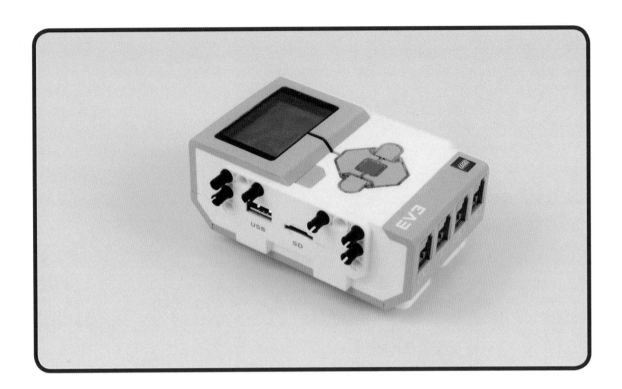

TOUCH SENSOR ASSEMBLY

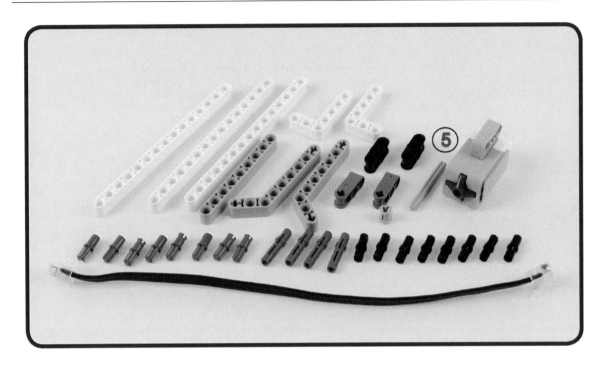

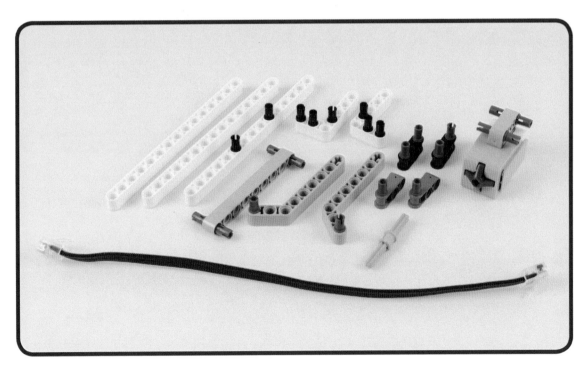

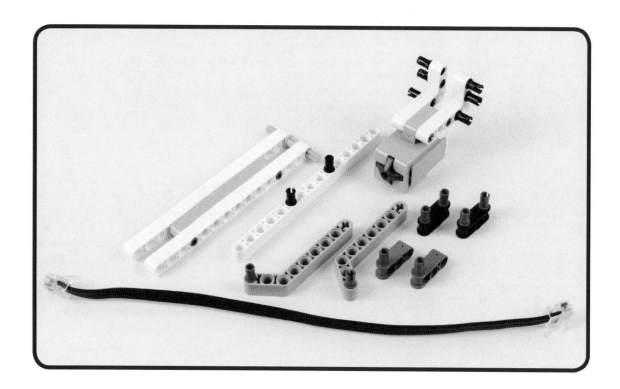

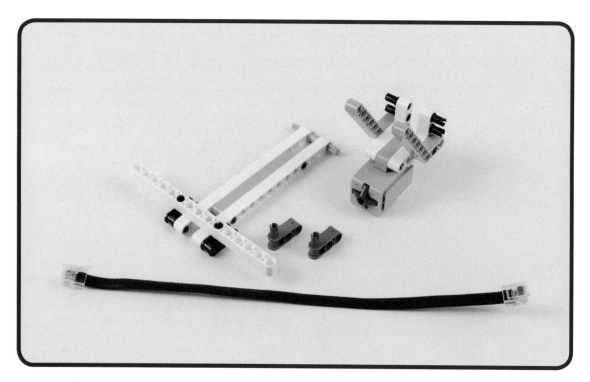

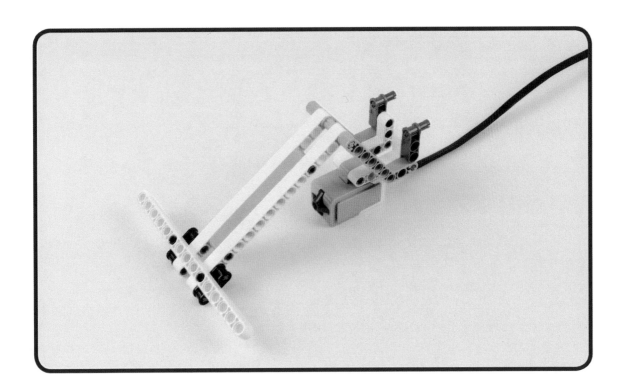

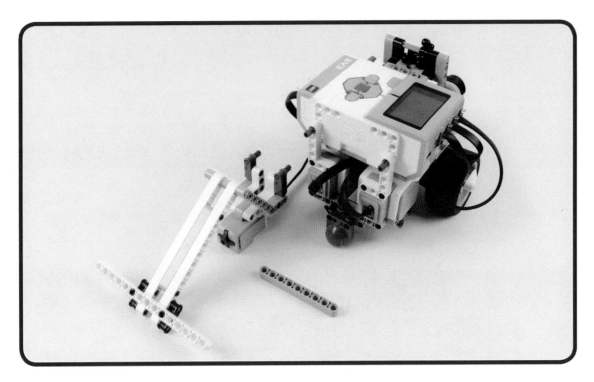

GYRO SENSOR ASSEMBLY

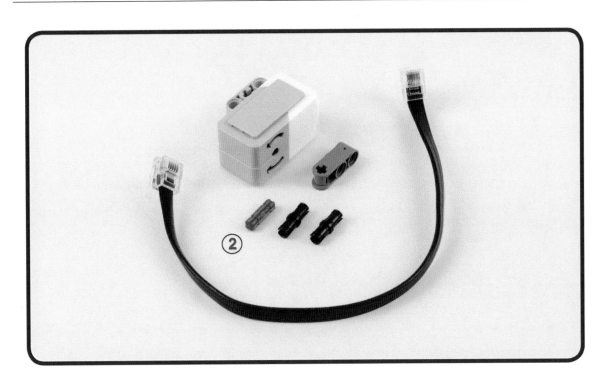

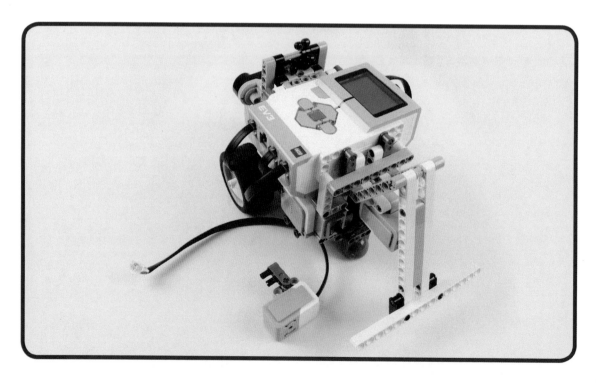

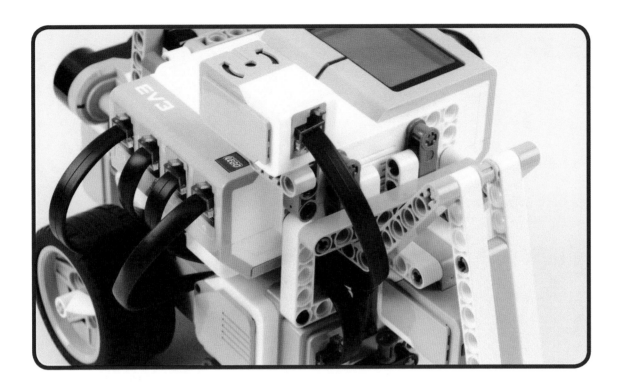

Now it is time to learn how to program!

5

Introduction to Programming

For many students, learning how to program is both exciting and scary. This introduction to programming is meant to be easy to understand. Once students have a solid foundation in the different programming blocks, they will be able to create more advanced programs. Some myths surround programming:

1. Computer programming is hard.

2. It is meant for geeks and nerds.

3. You need certain innate ability to program.

None of this is true. In fact, learning to programming is fun. We make decisions every day: some simple decisions, such as what to eat, or more difficult ones, such as where to invest. Whether a decision is easy or difficult, we follow logic to arrive at our conclusion. This is pretty much at the heart of programming. So everyone can learn to program. Becoming an expert programmer requires hard work and practice, just like it takes time to become an expert in in any field. But acquiring basic programming skills is easy and fun.

You can easily help your students to overcome the fear of programming by starting it right:

Talk to your students about how we communicate. Some students in your class may speak a second or even a third language. Ask them what languages they speak. Emphasize that we need to speak in English to understand each other, as that is our common language here in the U.S. If we want to go to Sweden and live there for a while, it will be nice to know the Swedish language so we can communicate with everyone.

Similarly, if we want computers to do what we want, we have to communicate our instructions to the computer in a language it can understand. As people can understand different languages, so can computers. The good news is: computer languages, such as Python, C and Java, are easier to learn than human ones. In our class, we will learn a graphical programming language that helps us to communicate with our EV3 brick.

STUDENT LEARNING OUTCOMES

- To develop working EV3 programs;
- To explain how each programming block works;
- To demonstrate their work by programming their robots to perform specified tasks.

What is an algorithm?

An algorithm is a strategy that lays out a clear, step-by-step procedure to solve a problem. This is really planning; algorithms are not programming.

What is a program?

For our robot to do what we want, we have to program it. The program is a sequence of instructions that controls the robot's function. Keep in mind that, in general, there is more than one way to program a robot.

What is graphical programming?

This is a programming language in which graphic icons are used to create the program, instead of text.

What is coding?

These days, we often hear the word "code" instead of, or in addition to, the word "programming." People will argue endlessly about the difference between these words. We will not worry about those subtleties.

Programming User Interface: Project and Programs

Unlike the NXT Mindstorms, the EV3 Mindstorms user interface uses the concept of project—an elegant approach. Student can create one project and have many programs under the same one. This eliminates the need to give each program a unique name in a classroom/center environment. Encourage your students to create a project with a unique name and to keep all of their programs under that name.

1. Open EV3 programming by double-clicking on the EV3 icon:

The following screen appears:

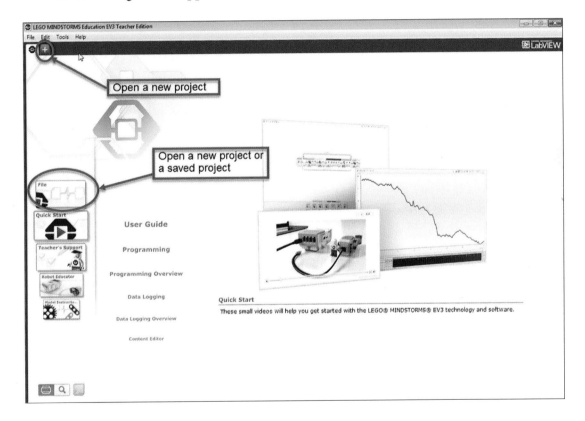

2. Add a project by clicking on the "+" sign.

3. Then 'Save Project As' using the 'File' menu option. (In this case, we saved the project as STEM.)

4. By default, the first program will be named 'Program. Double-click on the name and change the program name to something meaningful. We will write a program to make our robot to go straight, so I name this program as 'GoStraight'. In the following screen, you will see a project by name, STEM', and a program titled 'GoStraight'. Familiarize yourself with the screen and the various options available to you.

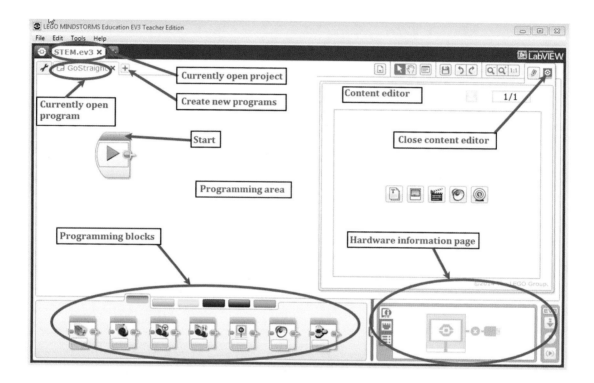

5. Discuss the 'File' menu option, the programming area, the programming blocks area, the hardware information window, the project name, the program name, and closing the 'Content Editor' area.

   a. **The 'File' menu option** is typically used for starting a new project, opening an existing project, and saving either one.

   b. **The programming area** is where we will create our program—and this is perhaps the most important area. We want it to be as big as possible, so we close 'Content Editor' by clicking on the button on the far right top.

   c. **The programming blocks area** has six categories and is color-coded. We will drag-and-drop blocks from here to the programming area to create our programs.

    d. **The hardware information window** shows us what is connected to the EV3 brick and to see its status. Keep an eye on it. We will use the download arrow from this window often. This window will be active only when your EV3 brick is connected.

6. Instructors need to understand how to download firmware from the 'Tools' menu.

    a. Firmware is a piece of software that is already on your brick. Normally you don't need to do anything about it. However, sometime firmware may be corrupt, or may have to be updated (when you use a newer version of the software). You can choose the 'Firmware Update' option form the tools menu and follow the direction to update your brick.

7. Discuss the six sets of programming blocks briefly.

    a. To make programming easier, this software divides all programming blocks into six categories. This makes programming process easy. We will use only the Action Blocks in the first session.

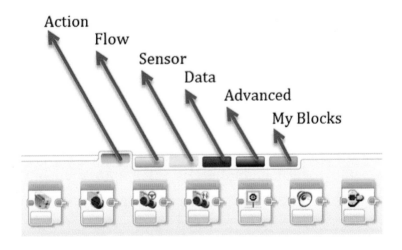

8. Action Blocks: There are 7 Action Blocks, numbered from left to right: (a) Medium motor; (b) Large motor; (c) Move steering; (d) Move tank; (e) Display; (f) Sound; (g) Brick status light.

Action blocks

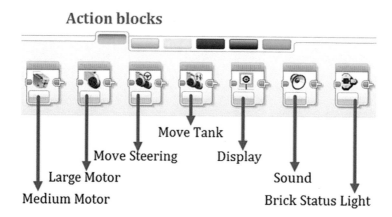

a. The Medium Motor (port A) and Large Motor blocks allow us to control one single motor. Medium Motor blocks run faster but provide lower torque. Large Motor blocks run slower but provide higher torque. Let us take a look at the move blocks. There are two in EV3.

b. The Move Steering block controls and regulates two motors (B and C) with a steering input and single power level: (+) steering = right; (-) steering = left.

c. The Move Tank block controls two motors with individual power level to each motor. This is an extremely useful block when you want to control the motors independently. We will use the Move Steering block in this unit. (We will demonstrate the Move Tank block in the next section.)

9. Every EV3 program must begin with a Start block, which starts the sequence of operations when you run a program. You do not need to do anything to create it, because it is already in the programming area when you start the software. However, if you have accidentally erased it and want it back, you can drag it from the Flow blocks.

10. Let us create a simple program by dragging the Move Steering block and placing it by the Start block. Make sure the Move Steering block snaps into the Start block. Your program should look like this:

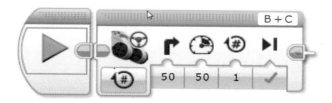

a. Understanding the Move Steering block:

Motors B and C are selected by default and shown in the little window on the top right corner.

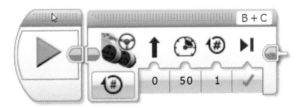

This is the duration option. Duration allows us to turn the motor off until some condition is met, on for a certain amount of time, and on for degrees or rotations. For the first program, we will use 'On' for the rotations option.

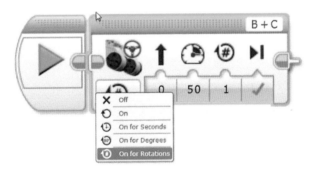

Use the slider to set the steering values so your robot can go straight or turn right or left. The neutral position (0) indicates that both wheels spin at the same speed. Depending upon how far the slider is moved from the neutral position, the robot will make a curve or a sharp turn.

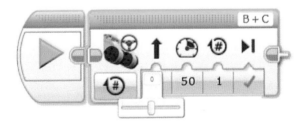

This indicates the power level: 0, being no power, is applied to 100, being full power. Moving the slider up makes the robot go forward and moving the slider down makes the robot go backward.

The next option allows you to enter the number of rotations. The default value is 1 rotation.

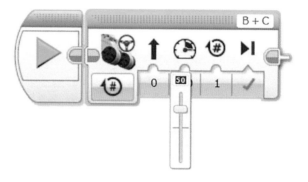

The last option is to choose Brake or Coast. The Brake option stops the robot immediately. The Coast option cuts power off to the wheel so the wheel stops eventually but not instantaneously.

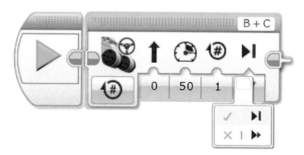

b. Now it is time to test our program. Make sure your robot is connected to the computer. Use the cable that came with your robot kit: one end goes into the computer USB port, the other into the PC port on your EV3 brick. Wait for a few seconds to make sure the computer is communicating with the brick. If you are connecting your brick for the first time, it may take a bit longer, and you may have to update the firmware. When the brick is connected, the Download arrow option will be available. You can use any of the three-options below to run your code, but I recommend just the Download one, using the arrow point down (see figure below, left). This option sends the program to your brick, and then you execute it from the brick. (If you choose any of the other two options, the program will execute immediately, and your robot may fall off your table.)

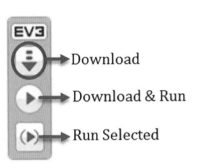

c.   To run the program, go to your brick. Use your arrow key to go to the 'File' option, look for your project (STEM, in this case) and then choose the program (GoStraight, in this case) under your project. If all goes well, your robot will move. Hold it in your hand and watch how its wheels spin. Use the wheel pointer (shown above, right) to see how far and in which direction the wheel spins.

Mission 1: Making my robot move!

Once you have discussed the programming interface with your students and shown them how to make the robot move, give your students the first task: ***Make your robot go straight for 60 cm.*** Students can use rotation or degree for this exercise. Some students may use the time, which may work well. Use start and finish lines so students can start consistently at the same location each time. Create a course using tape on the floor (or on vinyl) as shown below:

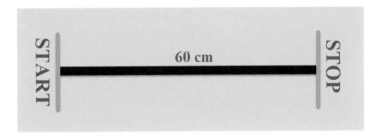

Give your students 10-15 minutes to do this activity. Do not help with the programming; you have already introduced it. If they go back and forth between the computer and the vinyl film, that is a very good sign.

Here is a sample program. I set the number of rotations to 4.5. Students may use rotations, or degrees, or even time. All answers are acceptable in this assignment as long as the robot covers the distance.

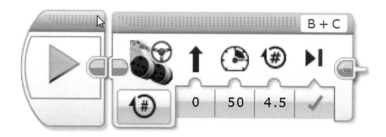

Mission 2: Movement with Calculations

Your students will be very happy once their robots move for the first time. (This activity is appropriate for students who are ready to learn (or already know) about the circumference of a circle and the value of pi [. Skip this if you are working with younger students.)

- Ask your students how accurately their robot covered the distance. Was it approximate, or very close?

- Ask them how can they make their robot to do the job more accurately. Tips: Some students will enter values in degrees and control the motion more accurately.

- What if your robot is traveling on a surface such as a tabletop (or on another planet on top of a rough terrain)? What if you robot is assisting a doctor with surgery and has to make an accurate incision? Are approximate answers acceptable, or do we want exact motion?

- Can you think of situations in which you want your robot to go exactly the same distance? In scenarios where we want accurate motion, we want to do some basic calculations.

Make your robot go straight for exactly 50 cm. To make the robot go the exact specified distance, we need to do some simple math, based on the wheel diameter. Ask your students to measure the diameter, which is actually printed on the side of the tire, but most of us do not notice this small writing. Let them still measure the diameter and verify it, for which your students will need a ruler. Besides, learning to take proper measurements is an important life skill, and this is a useful exercise that will also come in handy later on when your students learn how to use a caliper.

Calculations to make your robot go an exact distance in a straight line are shown below:

> **Step 1:** Find the diameter of the wheel. Use a ruler to measure.
>
> **Step 2:** Determine the circumference of your wheel. This is the distance your robot will travel for one rotation of the wheel. The formula for calculating the circumference is 2πr or πd.
>
> **Step 3:** Divide the distance your robot has to travel by the circumference of the wheel. The answer is the number of rotations one of your wheels must make for your robot to travel that distance in a straight line. Use this value in your Move Block, and watch your robot make precise movement. You can also convert the rotation to degrees by multiplying by 360 and use degrees in the Move Block.
>
> **Note:** Make sure you are using proper units. If necessary, you may have to convert. It is very common to specify the distance in meter (or feet) and the wheel diameter in millimeter (or inches).
>
> **Example:** Your robot must go forward 50 cm in a straight line.
>
> Step 1: The diameter of the wheel is 56 mm.
>
> Step 2: The formula for the circumference of a circle, C, is 2 π r = πd. In our case, C = π x 56 = 176mm.
>
> Step 3: 50 cm = 500 mm. $\dfrac{500}{176}$ = 2.84 *rotations* = 1023 *degrees*

After introducing students to this method (some students will even start doing this on their own during Mission 1), they should use this method to start all tasks.

> **NOTE**
>
> Even if your students make proper measurement and calculations, their robot may still be off due to friction, imperfections on the surface being used, and/or other conditions. However, starting off with calculations is the best way to begin with a good estimate. This method is typically used by all students in sixth grade and up, and by many fourth and fifth graders too. Once the circumference of a wheel is calculated, students can use this same value for all of their estimations of distance!

Even if students are simply using trial and error, you can still have them do this activity so they can practice varying the duration parameter to have their robot move a set amount of distance.

Sample program for Mission 2

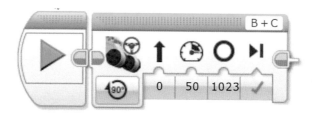

Notice: 1023 degrees in the programming block. Instead of choosing "On for Rotations," "On for Degrees" is selected for this option.

Mission 3: Movement with a little dance!

Have students program their robot to go forward for 40 cm and then spin continuously in place at the end. They can spin to the left or the right – that is up to them.

The purpose of this activity is to reinforce basic forward movement, introduce the steering aspect, and also practice varying the duration.

To spin the robot, students must turn it in one direction by moving the slider to the right or left. In the following example, the slider is moved all the way to the right.

Sample program for Mission 3

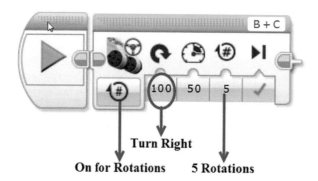

This program shows only the dance (spinning) part. Your robot will spin 5 times. Your first block must be a Move Block for going forward for 40 cm.

6

Getting Feedback

You program the robot to perform a series of tasks such as exploring a dark cave or navigating through an obstacle course. During this process you may want your robot to give you some feedback so you know everything is OK, or something is wrong, just as you want a family member to call you when s/he travels, to make sure everything is going well.

What is debugging?

Especially when writing a complex code, programmers often want to know where exactly the program is at a given time. In such situations, some form of feedback will be helpful. Traditionally programmers use text feedback that can be displayed on the computer screen.

We can do the same with EV3 brick by displaying text on the LCD screen. Sometimes it is difficult to see the little screen, so you may want to play a sound, or even your own voice. Audio feedback is fun and useful, but not effective in a noisy environment. In such cases, we can use EV3 LED lights, which are bright and can be seen from several feet away. We will explore all three options in this unit.

STUDENT LEARNING OUTCOMES

- To use Sound, Display and Brick Status Light blocks in their programs;
- To learn what sound is and how it propagates;
- To record their own voices and use them in their programs.

What is sound?

We use sound to communicate. Sound is a pressure wave that a vibrating object creates and that propagates through a medium such as air or water. A sound wave is analogous to ripples on a lake created by a stone thrown into the water: the rings of waves expand and reach the beach. Sound acts just like that.

Decibel (dB) is an expression that serves as the measure of sound. Below are examples of sound levels in decibels:

- Quite living room or soft whispering – 25 dB
- Refrigerator humming – 40 dB
- Normal conversation – 60 dB
- Passing motorcycle – 95 dB
- Someone screaming – 100 dB
- Air-raid siren – 120 dB
- Instant damage to eardrum – 160 Db

Although your robot kit does not come with a sound sensor, you can buy a Lego® compatible sound sensor, which can be used to measure various sound levels.

- Can you imagine a world without sound?
- Is there sound on the moon?

Sound Block

The Sound Block is fun, so introduce it as early as possible. A sound editor allows students to record their voice and play it later. Sound is also useful as a feedback when programming.

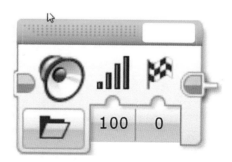

Sound Block lets you choose one of three options: Play File, Play Tone, or Play Note.

When the Play File option is selected, the top white space appears, letting the user choose a file. Built-in LEGO® sound files give the user numerous options. In addition, if the user records any custom sound file, it will be available under project files.

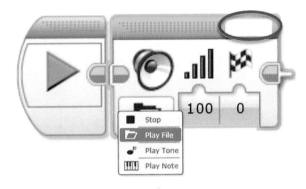

You can ask your students to create different sound effects using the available sound files. Look at the example below.

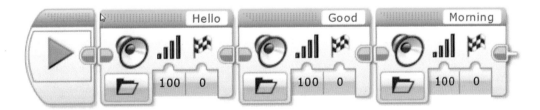

This program will say "Hello, Good Morning" by playing three different sound files. The Sound Block lets you adjust the sound level (100 is the loudest). it also has options to wait for completion, or to play just once and repeat. The following program will make a steady "Go" sound while the motor does 3 rotations:

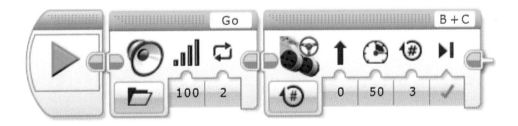

Sound Editing

At this point, also show students how to record their own sounds from the Sound Editor option (if you would like it to be used in your classroom). From the 'Tools' menu, open the Sound Editor, which lets you record and store your voice for use inside EV3 programs. After recording the sound, make sure you save it, using a meaningful file name.

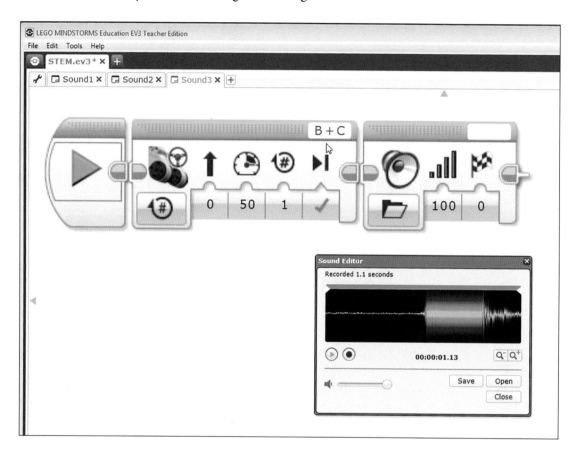

Play Tone and Play Note

The Play Tone option lets you play a tone of a specified frequency, which you can choose from the list of standards, or type in a number. The Play Note option lets you choose a note from a piano keyboard control. I am not into music and do not know how to use these options well. Let your students play with the Sound Block. They will come up very interesting and ingenious sound effects.

Mission 4: Movement with Sound!

Program your robot to make a greeting sound. Go straight for 40 cm while making a sound, and conclude with a celebratory sound.

Display Block

Demonstrate to students how to use the Display Block to show text or an image on the LCD screen. The Display Block is very useful for providing text feedback. For example, your EV3 can:

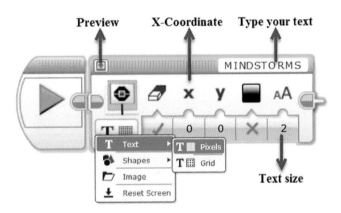

- figure out how far it traveled, and display the distance;

- figure out the color, and tell you what it is;

- do some complex calculations and show you the answer;

- or simply display a fun image after completing a task.

The Display Block mode lets you display text, shapes (line, rectangle, circle, point) and images. Like the Sound Block, you can create your own images or use available ones.

To place a text, e.g., "Hello," on the screen, you can type the coordinate for *x*, which changes from 0 to 177 and *y*, which changes from 0 to 127. Instead of typing numbers and trying to figure out the location, I recommend using the sliders for *x* and *y* to adjust the text location and preview its final appearance, per the figure below. Notice that the word "Hello" is typed into the white space, the preview mode is on, and the slider for adjusting the *y* coordinate is on. The *x* location is already adjusted. Also notice the Wait Block

(see below) with two seconds' wait at the end. This will allow the text to stay for two seconds.

Students can play with shape and graphic displays on their own. Look at the following sample code, with 'Preview' turned on:

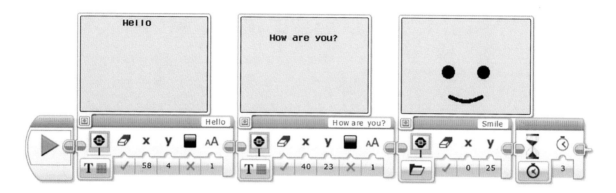

A challenge to using the Display Block is that the display changes so instantly you cannot see what is on the screen, because we have not communicated with EV3 on how long the display should remain visible.

Wait Block

But we can do so by using a Wait Block, which looks like an hourglass and is available under the 'Flow' category, as shown below.

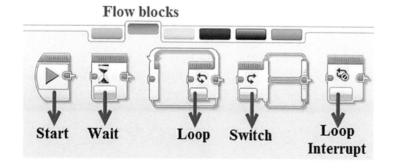

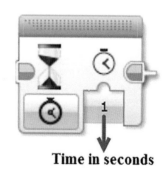

Time in seconds

You can specify how long to wait (one second, in this case) before moving to the next step in the sequence. The Wait Block can wait for a certain amount of time, or for a change in a sensor value. (We will discuss how to wait for the sensor input later.)

To display the text/graphics being displayed on the EV3 screen, all you have to do is to add a Wait Block for a specified amount of time in seconds.

Brick Status Light Block

This handy feature gives visual output before, during and after the execution of a program. LED lights are bright, and you can see them from several feet away.

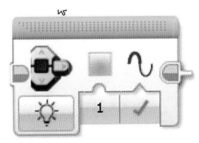

The Brick Status Light Block can be on one of the following modes:

- On
- Off
- Reset

The reset mode returns the Brick Status Light to the standard green blinking pattern, which indicates that a program is running.

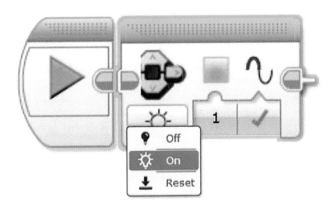

The Brick Status Light Block has three colors from which to choose.

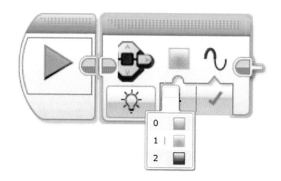

The light will pulse on and off when true.
The light will stay on constantly when false.

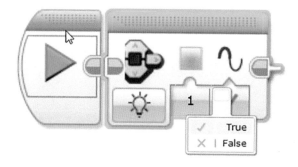

Mission 5: Movement with Lights!

Make your robot go straight for 60 cm while blinking the Brick Status Light.

Sample program – The following program make the robot go forward for 3 rotations while the Brick Status Light pulses on and off.

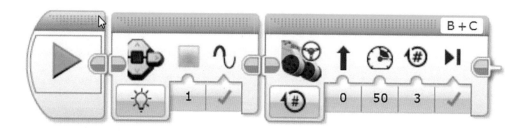

7

Making Turns

Now that you know how to make your robot go straight, it's time to learn how to program it to make turns. Your robot should be able to make various turns—left turn, right turn, swing turn, point turn, etc.—to accomplish its mission successfully.

STUDENT LEARNING OUTCOMES

- To make their robot make various turns accurately;
- To show the difference between swing turns and point turns.

Making Turns Using the Move Steering Block

Programming our robot to turn is a bit different from how we turn our car. Cars have one engine, and the motion from the engine crankshaft is transferred to the wheels. In cars, two front wheels can rotate at different speeds thanks to a device called, differential (a special set of gears). In robotics this gets too complicated so we use two motors, one for each wheel. It is like having two engines in a car. This allows us to control each wheel's speed. The Move Steering Block adjust the wheel speeds automatically for us.

There are two basic ways to make turns:

1. **Swing Turn:** To make a swing turn, stop one motor and spin the other, by moving the steering slider to 50 or -50. One wheel will turn and other wheel will not, and the robot will turn about a point on the stopped wheel.

2. **Point Turn:** In this case, make both motors spin in opposite directions at the same speed, by moving the slider to 100 or -100. One wheel will move forward, the other backward; the robot will rotate about midpoint.

3. **Gradual Turn:** Both wheels rotate at different speeds. If the steering value is anything other than +100 or -100, one wheel will rotate faster than the other.

Using the Move Steering Block to make different turns

You have already used the Move Steering Block (see below) to make the robot move forward or backward. This block can be used to make either a swing turn or a point turn. When the steering value is set at zero, the robot will move straight. When set at negative values (steering slider on the left), the robot will turn left. When set at positive values, the robot will turn right.

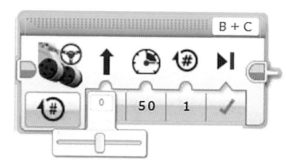

Demonstrate to your students how the robot turns when you move the steering slider to an extreme position. Show how to change the angle so the robot can make a 90° turn. Students can figure this out experimentally. The Move Steering Block is easy to use, as it takes care of managing two motors with just one block. All beginners should use the Move Steering Block for all practical purposes.

Experiment with turns – Swing Turn

1. Refer to the diagram below left. To make a 90° swing turn, drag-and-drop a Move Steering Block.

2. Refer to the figure on the right. Set the following options:

   a. Motor on for degrees.

   b. Change steering to 50 from 0, either by typing or by using the slider.

   c. Set the power to 20 (we want the wheel to move slowly so you can actually see it in motion).

   d. Make sure the amount of movement is set to 360 degrees.

Demonstrate this step by step to the students. When you run the program, the robot will turn slowly by 90°. Ask your students to watch how only one wheel is spinning and the other wheel is stationary in a swing turn. You can use the wheel pointer to show this. Your robot should make a nice 90° turn under normal conditions. If needed, you can change 360° to adjust the turn.

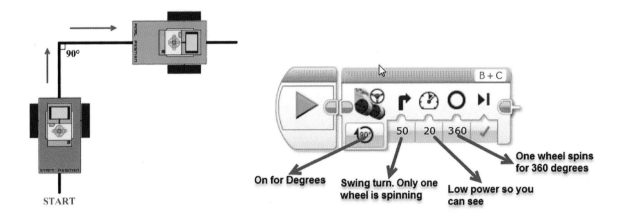

90° Swing Turn

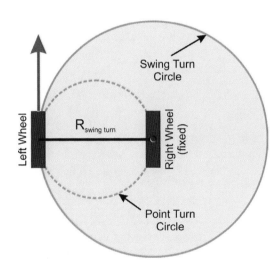

Swing Turn

One wheel rotates; the other is stationary. The radius of rotation is the distance between the wheels.

Experiment with turns: Point Turn

1. Refer to the diagram on the left. To make a 90° point turn, first drag-and-drop a Move Steering block.

2. Refer to the figure on the right. Set the following options:

    a. Motor on for degrees.

    b. Change steering to 100 from 0, either by typing or by using the slider.

    c. Set the power to 20 (we want the wheel to move slowly so you can actually see it in motion).

    d. Make sure the amount of movement is set to 180 degrees.

Demonstrate this step by step to the students. When you run the program, the robot will turn slowly by 90°. Ask your students to watch both wheels turning in opposite directions in a point turn. You can use the wheel pointer to show this. Your robot should make a nice 90° turn under normal conditions. If needed, you can change 180° to adjust the turn.

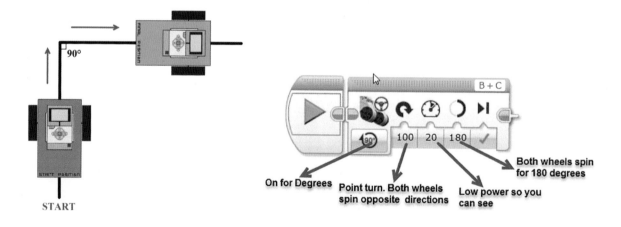

90° Swing Turn

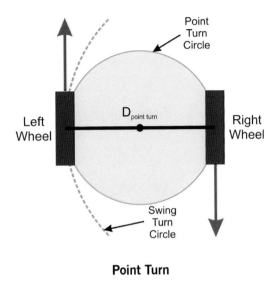

Point Turn

> **NOTE**
>
> Both wheels of the robot turn in opposite directions at the same speed. The radius is ½ of the distance between the wheels. The point turn has a smaller radius than the swing turn.

What is the biggest difference between the two turns and, which one to use?

The swing turn requires a large turning radius, which can be measured from the distance between the two wheels. The point turn requires half the radius of the swing turn; the robot rotates about an axis in-between the two wheels. Use whichever one you like, but the point turn will help your robot negotiate tight spaces, as it needs less room.

Experiment with turns: Gradual Turn

Instead of using 50 as the value for steering in the swing turn, say, you choose 30: both wheels of your robot will rotate in the same direction at different speeds. This type of turn will be useful if you want your robot to follow a circular path. Try it yourself.

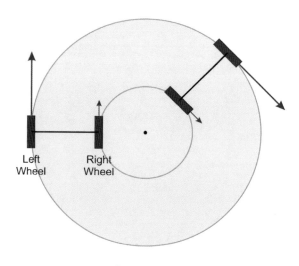

Gradual Turn

> **NOTE**
>
> Both wheels of the robot are turning at different speeds.

Mission 6: Move

Create a course with tape on the floor (or on vinyl) as shown at right. Let your students attempt this program for 10-15 minutes. Do not give them answers if they are having trouble; guide them in the right direction.

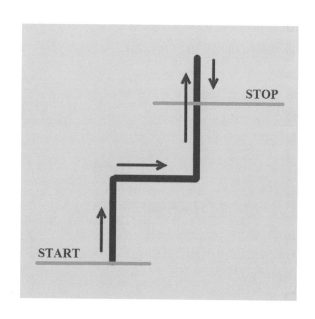

1. Go forward 30 cm at 50% speed

2. Make a right turn (90°)

3. Go forward 30 cm at 50% speed

4. Make a left turn (90°)

5. Go forward 40 cm at 50% speed

6. Backup 20 cm at 100% speed

7. Make a celebratory sound

Sample Move Program

Notice how blocks can be connected to reduce space. Each block is commented for clarity.

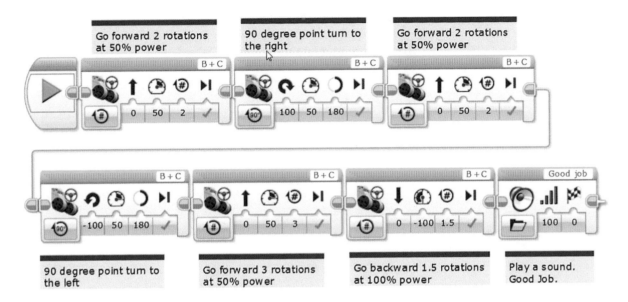

Understanding Turns Better: Using the Move Tank Block

The Move Steering Block lets you control two motors at the same time. It can do everything: drive forward, backward, turn, and stop. The Move Tank Block gives you more flexibility than Move Steering, letting you control each motor individually. Look at the blocks in the side-by-side comparison shown below:

Move Steering	Move Tank
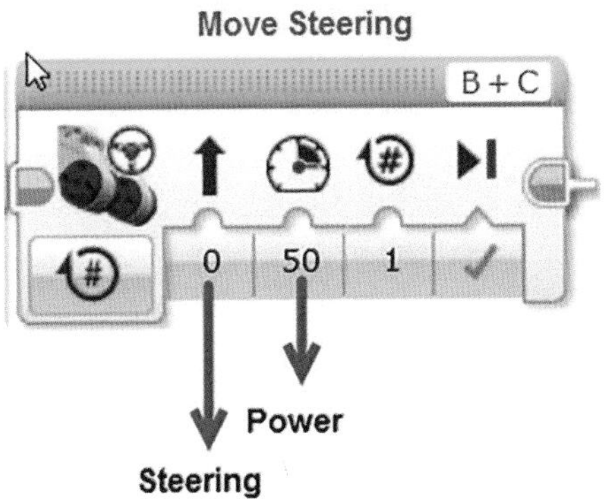	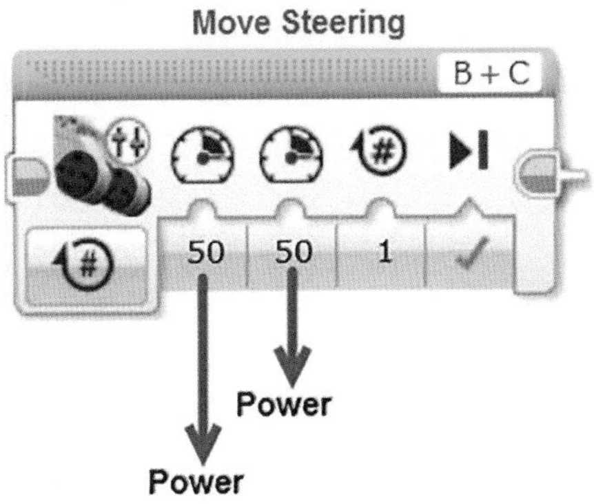
Easier to use.	

Note: The steering port lets you go staright, or turn left or right, by giving only one power input, even though we have two motors.	**Note:** No steering option. Steering is controlled by changing the power in both motors. If you give both motors the same power, the robot goes straight. If one motor has 0 power, then the robot will make a swing turn. To make a point turn, you must give equal but opposite power to the motors.

I highly recommend you introduce the Move Tank block to your students. I have seen second graders use it with ease. It is very useful in the following programs. However, you can skip this block if pressed for time.

Swing turn: This is made by stopping one wheel and spinning the other. Then the robot will effectively pivot about the stopped wheel. Let us make a right swing turn to make your robot turn exactly 90°:

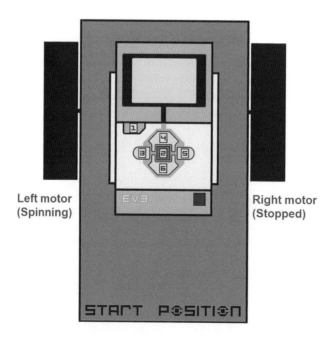

Left motor (Spinning)   Right motor (Stopped)

Your robot with two front driving wheels is shown above. This is the start position. To make a right turn, you have to program your left motor to move and right motor to stop. We will use Move Tank block so we can control the power of both motors.

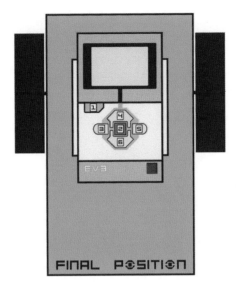

To make things clear, we will use a different color, Green for final position as shown above.

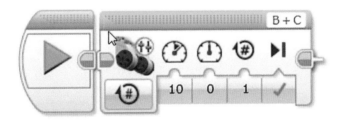

This EV3 program shows the Move Tank Block, in which the power for the left motors is set to 10 and the right motor to 0. Currently it shows 1 rotation for the left motor. The power level is set to a very small value so you can observe the turn. To make a 90° turn, we must make some calculations, as discussed earlier.

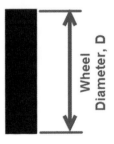

Wheel diameter = 56 mm. Students are required to measure the diameter. In LEGO® tires, this dimension is printed on the side of the tire itself. Pi = $\frac{22}{7}$ Wheel circumference = $2.pi.R_{wheel}$ = 176 mm.

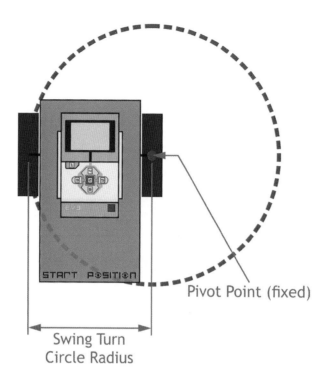

Pivot Point (fixed)

Swing Turn
Circle Radius

Measure the distance between the wheels. This will be your spin circle radius. I measured 120 mm.

Spin circle radius (distance between the wheels) = 120 mm;
Spin circle circumference = $2.pi.R_{spin}$ = 754.28 mm.

If you look the diagram on the left carefully, you will see that in order to make a 90° turn, your left wheel must travel quarter of the spin circle circumference. So that will be $\frac{754.3}{4} = 188.6$ mm.

To determine the rotations to be made by the left motor, we divide the distance to be traveled by the left wheel by its circumference. No. of rotations for left wheel =

$$\frac{Distance\ to\ be\ traveled\ by\ the\ wheel}{Wheel\ circumference} = \frac{188.6}{176} = 1.07\ rotations = 385\ degrees$$

The corresponding EV3 program is shown on the left.

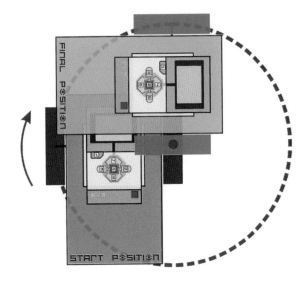

Final position. Notice the pivot point (in Red), which remained stationary.

Point turn: A point turn is made when both wheels rotate in opposite directions at the same speed. When this is done, the robot will effectively pivot about center-point. Let us make a right point turn to make your robot turn exactly 90°. The point turn is extremely useful in tight areas, as it uses very minimal space.

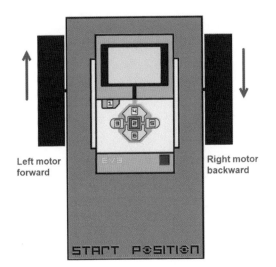

Your robot with two front driving wheels is shown on the left. This is the start position. To make a right turn, program your left and right motors to move at the same speed in opposite directions. We will use the Move Tank Block to control the power of both motors.

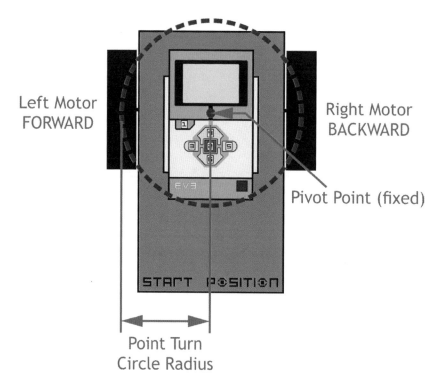

Left Motor
FORWARD

Right Motor
BACKWARD

Pivot Point (fixed)

START POSITION

Point Turn
Circle Radius

Measure the distance between the wheels. This will be your spin circle radius. I measured 120 mm.

Spin circle diameter (distance between the wheels) = 120 mm. So the radius is 60 mm.
Spin circle circumference = 2.pi.R_{spin} = 377.14 mm.

If you look the diagram carefully, you will see that, to make a 90° turn, your left and right wheels have to travel for a quarter of the spin circle circumference in opposite directions. So that will be $\dfrac{377.14}{4}$ = 94.3 mm .

To determine the rotations to be made by the left motor, we divide the distance to be traveled by the left wheel by its circumference.

No. of rotations for each wheel =

$$\frac{Distance\ to\ be\ traveled\ by\ the\ wheel}{Wheel\ circumference} = \frac{188.6}{176} = 1.07\ rotations = 385\ degrees$$

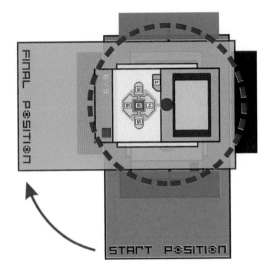

Final position. Notice the pivot point (in Red), which remained stationary.

Mission 7: Go around a circle

Program your robot to go around an 80 cm diameter circle. You can use either the Move Steering Block or the Move Tank Block. Specify enough rotations so the robot can complete the circle.

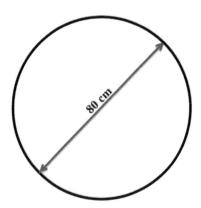

Mission 8: Robot Slalom Challenge

- Design, build and program an autonomous robot that will slalom through flags.
- Your robot must play celebratory song after crossing the finish line.
- Your robot must go around the outside of the flags.
- You will be penalized if the robot hits a flag.
- The robot that completes the course in the fastest time wins the challenge.

Slalom Course Options:

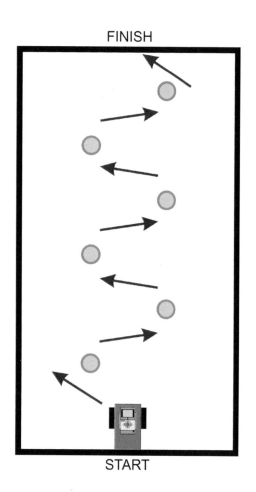

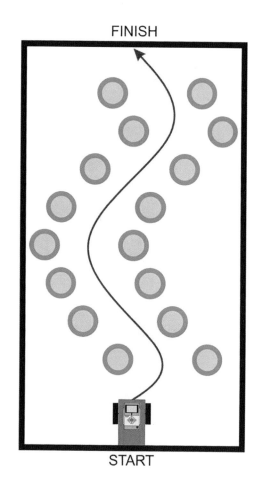

8

Learning to Loop

Doing the same thing over and over again is often very important but can be boring and can lead to mistakes. Fortunately, robots never get tired of doing the same thing again and again. In this lesson, we are going discuss how to make your robot to do the same thing repeatedly using loop. Loop is the single most important concept in programming. If you want your robot to do the same thing repeatedly, normally you will keep using the same block again and again. For example, if you want your robot to make the same sound over and over, drag-and-drop the Sound Block as many times as you need. Yet this is not the best way to do it; not only is it time consuming, but it takes more memory, it is boring, and it wastes time and resources.

A better way to do this is a special command to do the same thing over and over: the Loop Block, which performs a series of commands repeatedly. It can be used for a certain amount of time (seconds), a certain number of times (#), or on certain conditions (e.g., pushing a button). It is one of five Flow Blocks (below).

STUDENT LEARNING OUTCOMES

- To explain and use Flow Blocks in a program;
- To use the Start, Loop and Wait Blocks in their codes.

Flow Blocks

The Flow category comprises five programming blocks, as shown below: (1) Start Block, (2) Wait Block, (3) Loop Block, (4) Switch, (5) Loop Interrupt.

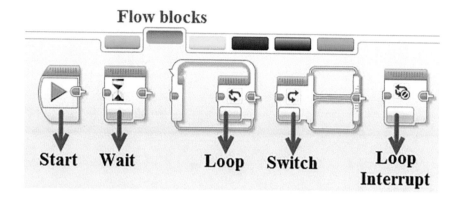

Flow blocks

Start   Wait   Loop   Switch   Loop Interrupt

Start Block: This indicates the beginning of a program, or a sequence of instructions. In EV3, you can actually have more than one Start Block, so you can execute two or more programs at the same time. We will explore parallel programming later. In the following lesson we will use just one Start Block.

Wait Block: In this example, the Wait Block waits for one second before moving to the next block in the sequence. It can wait for a certain amount of time, or for a change in a sensor value.

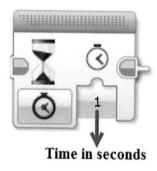

Time in seconds

Loop Block:

Options:

Unlimited – In the unlimited mode, the loop is repeated forever. The only way to stop the loop would be to use the back button on the brick. Blocks placed after this loop will not be executed. so do not create blocks after such a loop.

Count – When the count mode is selected, the user will be able to specify how many times to repeat the blocks inside the loop.

Time – When the count mode is selected, the user will be able to specify the amount of time in seconds.

Logic – In the logic mode, the loop will continue to execute until the input is true.

Sensor – EV3 includes several sensors, and the loop block contains corresponding modes that read sensor data and compare it to an input value. The figure shows various modes available within the loop. We will discuss these options under Mode as and when necessary.

Introduce the Loop Block to your students briefly, just showing unlimited/count and time options. You do not need to show other options at this time.

Also, show them how to write a program. A sample program is shown below, in which the robot goes forward 1 rotation and backward one rotation and the loop is repeated 2 times. The program ends with a sound (good job).

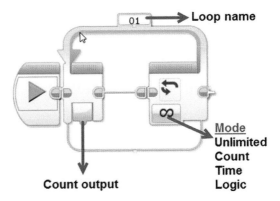

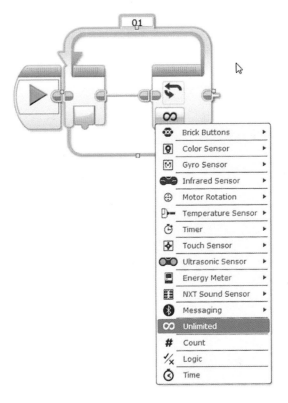

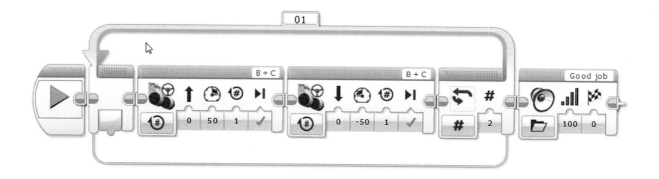

Mission 9: Go around a square

Ask your students

- What is a square?
- How do you make a robot go around a square?
- How many straight moves, and how many turns?
- If we program each move, how many blocks will be used?
- Is there a better way?

Making your robot follow a 20 cm square by repeated use of Move Steering or Move Tank blocks is inefficient, but let them do it if they want to—only make sure they learn to use the **Loop** Block (above).

> **NOTE**
>
> Instead of 20 cm, you can ask the students to use a tile (if the classroom floor has tiles) for a square.

Sample program for Square program

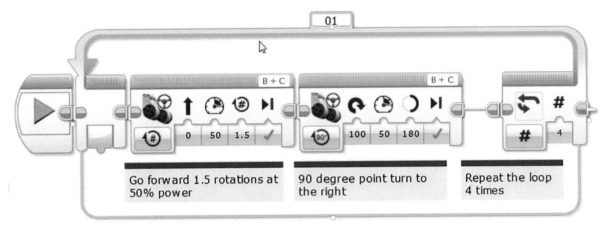

| Go forward 1.5 rotations at 50% power | 90 degree point turn to the right | Repeat the loop 4 times |

Mission 10: Equilateral Triangle

Write a program to make your robot to follow this equilateral triangle. Each side of the triangle is 25 cm.

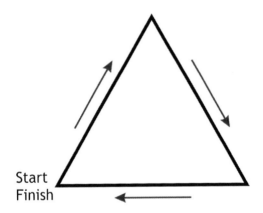

Start
Finish

> **NOTE**
>
> Students will easily figure out how to go forward but will take some time to figure out the turn (rotation).

Mission 11: Square inside a square (optional)

In this task, the goal is to make sure students are comfortable using a loop inside another loop.

Program the robot to follow a 20 cm square, then wait for 2 seconds, make a sound, complete a 30 cm square, wait for 2 seconds, make another sound, and repeat the entire process one more time.

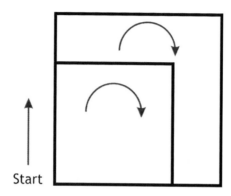

Sample Program for Mission 11:

Notice two loops in sequence and these two inside another external loop. Let the students figure this out. Also notice where the Wait and Sound blocks are placed.

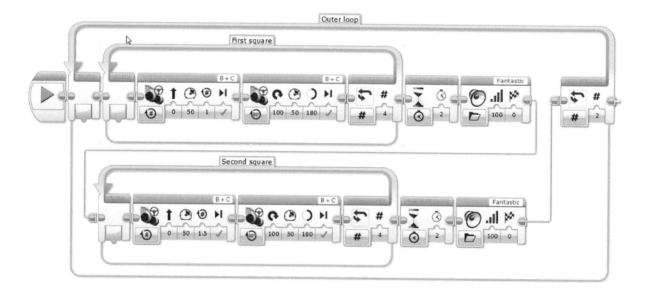

9

Using the Wait Block with the Ultrasonic Sensor Mode

We used the Wait Block earlier to delay the beginning of an upcoming activity or an ongoing process by a specified amount of time. The Wait Block is capable of much more than this simple delay; it comes with a rich set of functionalities. Each sensor type is available to choose from within the Wait Block. After choosing the appropriate sensor mode, you can wait for the sensor to reach a specified value or compare against a specified value. In this unit we will use the ultrasonic sensor mode.

STUDENT LEARNING OUTCOMES

* To use the ultrasonic sensor with the Wait Block to detect distance and take appropriate action.

Drag-and-drop the Wait Block into the programming area. The figure below shows how to choose the ultrasonic sensor mode, which creates more options. Select 'Compare Values' and 'Distance Centimeters.'

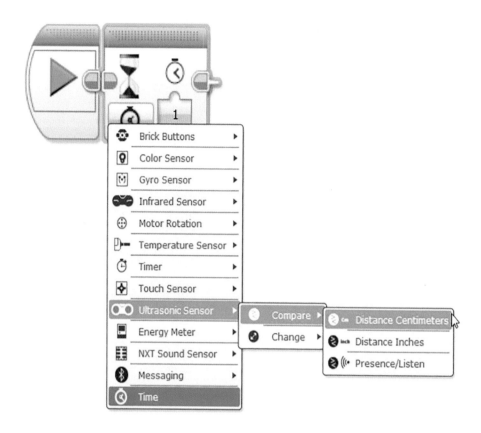

Once the selections are made, the Wait Block should look as shown in the figure below:

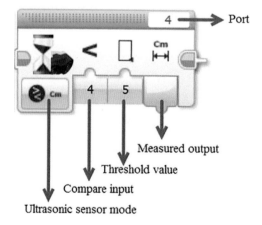

Detecting obstacles

So far we have selected the Move Steering Block for rotations or degrees so the robot could go a certain distance. In this situation, the robot would blindly try to go the specified distance; if an object were in front of it, our robot would not see it, but simply slam into it. This is not a smart robot. We want our robot to see objects in front of it and make smart decisions about them.

Our goal in this session, therefore, is to program our robot to go forward as long as possible until it sees any obstacle, then stop.

- We will use a Move Steering Block to make the robot go forward.
- We will choose the 'On' option, so our robot will keep going until an action takes place or a condition is met.
- We will use the Wait Block to wait for the ultrasonic sensor input. In the Wait Block, we will choose the 'Less Than' option for comparison and 20 cm as threshold value.
- When the ultrasonic sensor sees an object within 20 cm, the robot must stop. For this, we choose the Move Steering Block with the 'Off' option to stop.

A sample program for this is shown below. Demonstrate this to the students.

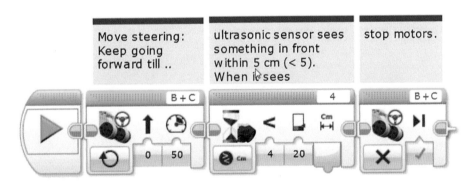

Mission 12: Keep your robot moving forward

Write a program to make your robot to keep moving forward until an obstacle is encountered. When this happens, your robot must stop, provide feedback (sound/display/light), and turn away from the object.

Sample program for Mission 12

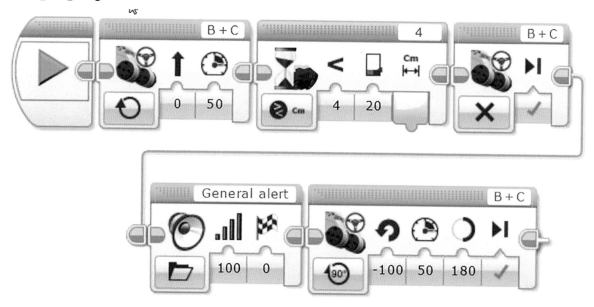

Mission 13: Wandering robot

Write a program to make your robot move around in an arena without running into any objects. This mission is similar to the last, except that the process must be continued indefinitely. Here is the basic logic:

- The robot goes forward until an obstacle (e.g., a wall) is detected. This requires a Move Steering Block and a Wait Block.

- Make a turn (you decide which direction to turn and how much you want to turn). This requires a Move Steering Block.

- Keep doing the above steps again and again. This requires the Loop Block. All the above blocks must be inside the loop.

- We have added the Brick Light Status Block to flash red whenever the robot encounters an obstacle.

Sample program for wandering robot

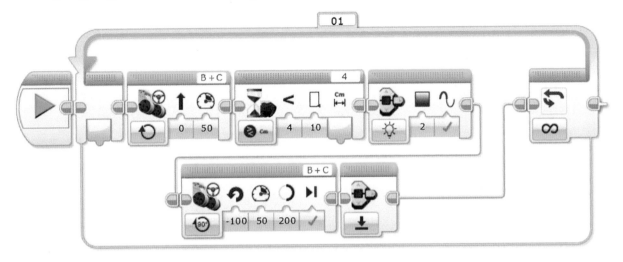

Points to discuss with students:

- How close do you want to go near an object?
- Do you need to reverse when you see an obstacle? Why, or why not? If so, how far do you need to reverse??

Area for wandering

You can set up an area for a wandering robot using the wall on two sides of your classroom, cardboard boxes, and other large objects to create an enclosed area. You can then place books and other items to serve as obstacles. You can modify this assignment in any that works for you: some instructors like to create one or two openings in the area, one for entering and one for exiting. So the robot enters at one location, navigates through the obstacles and exits the area through another opening successfully.

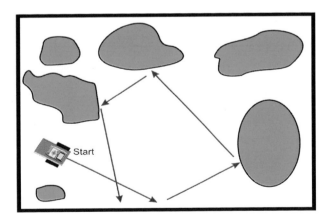

10

Using the Wait Block with Color Sensor

STUDENT LEARNING OUTCOMES

- To use the color sensor with the Wait Block, and to identify various colors;
- To program the robot to complete an activity using the color sensor.

Show your students how to use the color sensor to stop a robot when it sees a black line. The figure below shows the Wait Block with the options available for the color sensor. Let us choose the RLI option.

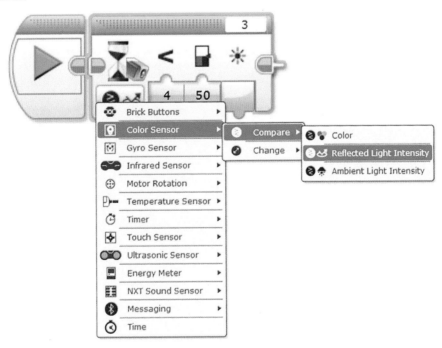

Detecting a Black Line

Our goal is to program our robot to go forward as long as possible until it sees a black line and stops.

- **To** accomplish this, use a strip of black tape on a surface distinctly different from black, such as a white surface.

- Put your robot on the white and black surface, and measure the RLI value from the black and white parts of the surface.

- Take a few readings for white and a few readings (at least three each) for black. Write them down in your notebook, and find the average value for black and white. (We will use this information in our program soon.)

  - Average value for black is _____ (Write down the value you calculated from your readings.)

  - Average value for white is _____ (Write down the value you calculated from your readings.)

- Let us now write the code.

  - We will use a Move Steering Block to make the robot go forward.

  - We will choose the 'On' option, so our robot will keep going until an action takes place or a condition is met.

  - We will use the Wait Block to wait for color sensor input. In the Wait Block, we will choose the 'Less Than' option for comparison and the average value for black. I will use the value 10 as the threshold value.

- When the color sensor sees a value below 10, the robot must stop. For this, we choose the Move Steering Block with the 'Off' option to stop.

A sample program for this is shown below. Demonstrate this to the students.

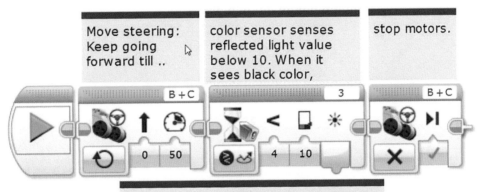

Note: I measured RLI value 10 for black.
You must make your own measurements

Mission 14: Stay in an enclosed area

This is a fun mission, and it sets the stage for a sumo event in which one robot must try to push the other robot out of the ring. The ring is a circular white area indicated by a black line. Write a program that will let your robot go around the circular area without going outside the black line. To make this interesting, you can put black tape around the edges of a table and require that the robot be always in motion and stay on the surface without falling off the tabletop, as shown in the figure below.

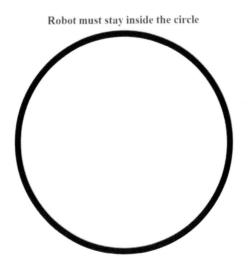

Robot must stay inside the circle

This mission is similar to the previous mission, in which your robot stops when it detects the black line. Simply use the same program, but back up the robot when it sees the black line, and turn the robot around. This whole procedure can be done within a loop. That's it.

Sample program for Mission 14

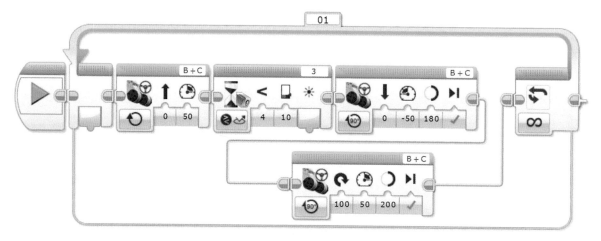

Using Reflected Light Intensity (RLI) Mode and Color Sensor Mode

We have used RLI to identify the colors white and black—a reliable method. If we want to separate only black and white, this is all we need. However, we often want to identify other colors, too. We can still use the same approach, because RLI values will be different for each color. However, the values may be close between colors, and your program logic to identify colors could become large with many conditional statements. We can avoid this if we use the color sensor option to determine colors directly. Let us use it to identify a few colors.

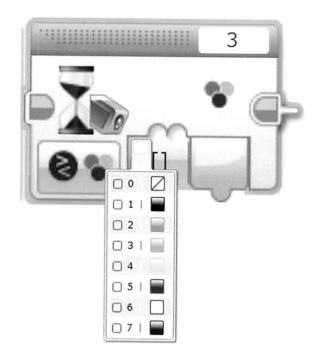

Let us drag-and-drop a Wait Block and select the color sensor option instead of the RLI option. Notice that we may now choose various colors. The color sensor can automatically detect seven colors. We do not need to measure reflected light for each of these colors, as each one is assigned a number. We can choose one or more colors from the list.

Mission 15: Stop at Red or Black

Self-driving cars are no longer the wave of the future. They are already here. How do we keep a car or our robot in a lane? One way is to identify the lines on both sides of the lane. For this mission, we have created a space (shown in yellow in the figure) between two circles. Your robot should move around this area indefinitely without crossing the red or black circle.

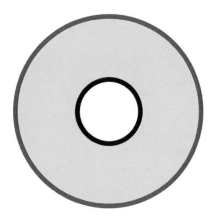

Sample program for Mission 15

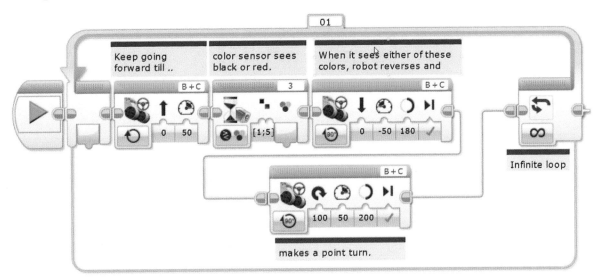

Mission 16: Stay in an enclosed area

Ask students to rewrite the program using the color sensor mode instead of RLI.

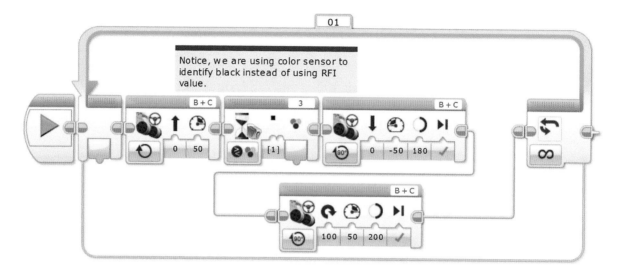

11

Using the Wait Block with Touch Sensor

Touch sensors are widely used in the industry, where they are often known as 'limit switches,' being used in control systems to determine whether an object has reached certain position. They are also used as safety devices to avoid accidents. For example, elevators and automatic doors use limit switches.

STUDENT LEARNING OUTCOMES

- To use the touch sensor in the program and make the robot respond to that action.

Our robot has an ultrasonic sensor, so it can see any obstacle in front—but not in back. So when it backs up, it may crash into something. Modern cars have cameras that enable us to see what is in back of us when we reverse the car. Since our robot has no such camera, we will use the touch sensor.

The Wait Block with touch sensor mode selected is shown in the figure below.

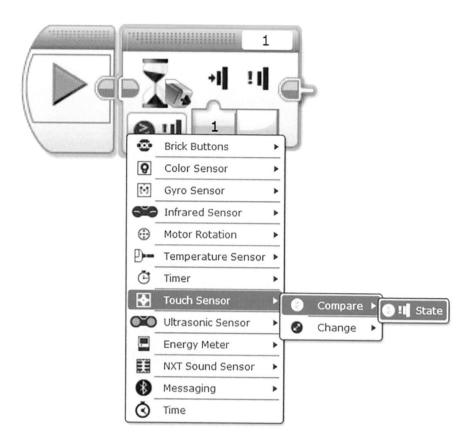

Let us use the touch sensor with a simple program first: to program our robot to move forward and stop when the touch sensor is pressed. This code will have a Move Steering Block and a Wait Block with a touch sensor. A sample program is below. Demonstrate this to your students.

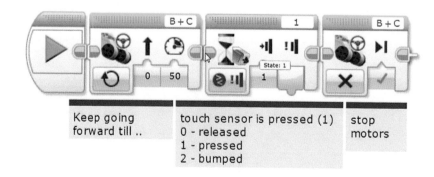

Keep going
forward till ..

touch sensor is pressed (1)
0 - released
1 - pressed
2 - bumped

stop
motors

Mission 17: Use the touch sensor to start your robot

Write a program that will start to give sound, then move your robot forward for one rotation.

Sample program for Mission 17

Notice, when you run the program, that nothing will happen until you press the touch sensor.

Mission 18: Using ultrasonic and the touch sensor to control the movement

We will now challenge our students to use two sensors. Write a program that makes the robot go forward until it sees something in front of it. You can wave your hand or let the robot sense an obstacle. When the robot senses something in front, it must back up until the touch sensor is pressed. Let the robot keep doing this. So you will have a funny robot that keeps going back and forth. (Refer to the figure below.)

Sample program for Mission 18

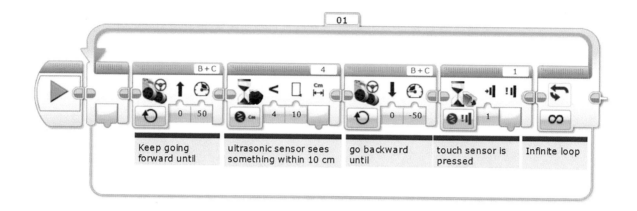

12

Using the Wait Block with Gyro Sensor

The gyro sensor, widely used in real-life applications from cell phones and aircraft to robots, helps us to sense angular rotation and changes in orientation. It is used in airplanes, drones and Segway to maintain stability. We can use it to make accurate turns and measure the change in the angular position of the robot. The gyro sensor's biggest advantage is that we do not have to perform any calculations for making turns.

STUDENT LEARNING OUTCOMES

- To use the gyro sensor to make accurate turns
- To measure the change in angular orientation

Important points to remember before using gyro sensor

- The gyro sensor is sensitive and must be motionless before the robot starts to move. Even pushing a button to start the program can impact the gyro sensor's performance. Gyro sensors have two commonly associated problems: drift and lag. The errors they cause can be minimized using advanced programming. When you use the gyro sensor, be gentle with the robot. Don't push/ shake it.

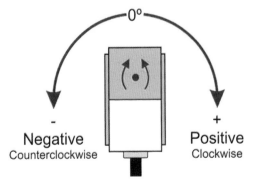

- Make sure the gyro sensor is mounted properly and level with the ground.

- Make sure the gyro sensor is correctly oriented. The axis is perpendicular to the two arrows shown on top of the sensor.

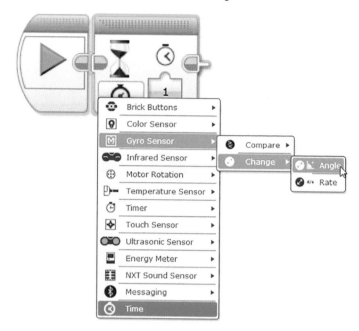

- Keep in mind that the EV3 gyro sensor is not as accurate as industrial sensors. The accuracy of EV3 gyro is -3 to +3 degrees. This error in measurement accumulates, so always reset the gyro sensor when using it in Comparison Mode. We will use Change Mode in this task.

- A trial-and error-approach is needed to determine the correct value for using a gyro sensor with your robot.

- The gyro sensor is directional; rotation of the sensor in the clockwise direction is considered positive, and counter clockwise is negative, as shown in the figure below.

- The Wait Block with its gyro sensor mode selected is shown in the figure below. Notice the compare option and change option; we will use the change option.

Sample program using the gyro sensor:

Program your robot to go forward 2 rotations. Make a 45° turn to the right, and then go forward 1.

   While this can be achieved by the Move Steering Block alone without using the gyro sensor, we will show how the gyro sensor can be used. The final outcome will look like the figure to the left.

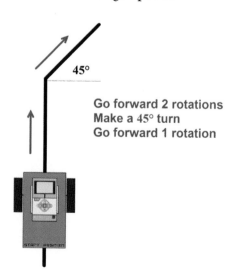

45°

Go forward 2 rotations
Make a 45° turn
Go forward 1 rotation

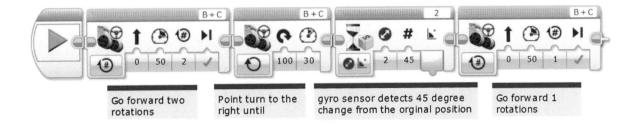

| Go forward two rotations | Point turn to the right until | gyro sensor detects 45 degree change from the orginal position | Go forward 1 rotations |

Mission 19: Trace the shape

Let your students measure the linear and angular measurement of a figure similar to the one to the left, or make your own diagram.

Students should use a ruler and a protractor to make the measurements. They should then write a program for their robot to follow the path from the start to the end using only the gyro sensor.

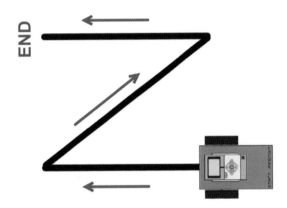

Sample program for Mission 19

The program will be similar to the earlier gyro program. Student will utilize Move Steering Blocks along with Wait Block using gyro sensor.

13

Using the Wait Block with Brick Buttons

As you have seen, the Wait Block can be used in numerous ways. You can now explore yourself on the various functionalities available with this block. We want to show you one more useful way to get the most out of the Wait Block.

STUDENT LEARNING OUTCOMES

- To use brick buttons in their programs to control the action flow.

How to use the Wait Block with Brick Buttons

Drag-and-drop a Wait Block and select the Compare → Brick Buttons option, as shown in the figure to the left.

After choosing the Brick Buttons mode, you may choose one of the five buttons on the brick, as shown in the figures below. You can also choose the status of the button if a button is pressed, released, or bumped.

Once you place the Wait Block at a location, your program will wait for you to push the appropriate button before it can proceed further. This is a simple yet extremely useful function for controlling your program.

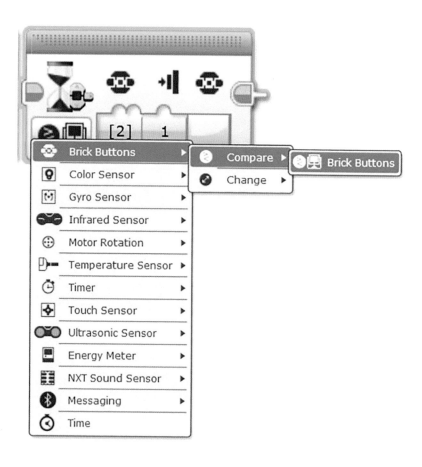

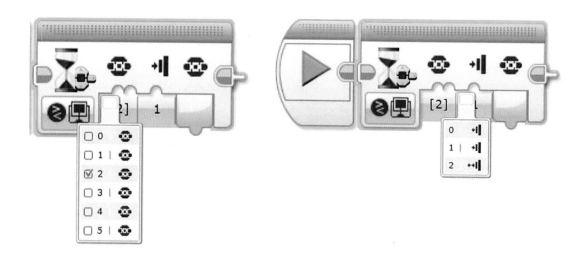

Sample Program

Let us say we want your robot to go a certain distance, and to wait for you to come there and tell the robot to go further. Basically, instead of waiting for a sensor input, the robot is waiting for you. This feature is also very useful in debugging problems.

Let us write a program to move the robot forward 3 rotations and then wait for you to come and push a button. When you push the button, it makes a sound, and then the robot makes a left turn. We will use the middle (enter) button for this exercise. It is always useful to display a message so we know the robot is waiting for your input. A sample program is shown below.

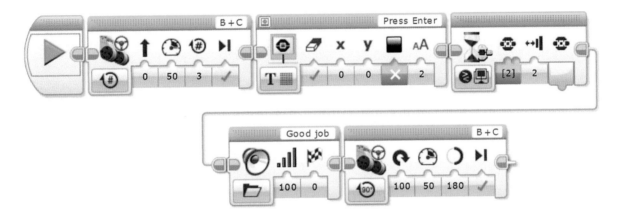

This program goes three rotations and displays a message, 'Press Enter.' When you press 'Enter,' the robot says, 'Good Job,' and takes a left turn.

14

Multitasking with EV3

Multitasking, parallel programming, and multi-threading are some of the common words used to describe the performance of many tasks simultaneously. In reality, however, EV3 processes each command one at a time, but at such a rapid rate we see several things happening at the same time.

STUDENT LEARNING OUTCOMES

- To write programs that require multiple tasks to be executed simultaneously;
- To isolate problems that emerge when multitasking;
- To recognize the usefulness of multitasking when making emergency stops, e.g., when the program has to stop all activities and come to a halt immediately.

Roaming around in an enclosed area

Put the robot in an enclosed area you already developed. This program is reproduced below.

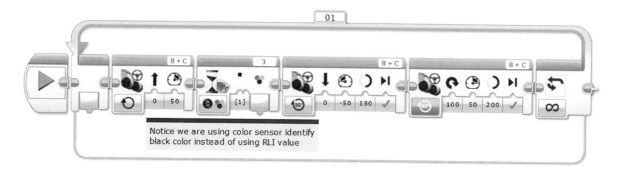

Notice we are using color sensor identify black color instead of using RLI value

In this example, our robot roams around inside a black circle. While this is going on, let us say we want our robot make a sound if it sees anything within 10 cm. We can include a Sound Block within the loop and choose option 1 or 2 to continue the sound. Refer to the Sound Block at right:

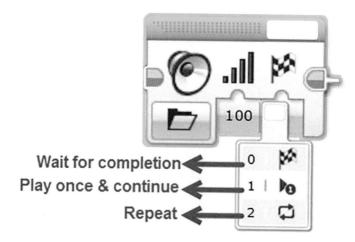

However, if we want to check for the ultrasonic sensor and play a sound when the robot sees something, we will certainly need to multitask. Look at the sample program below:

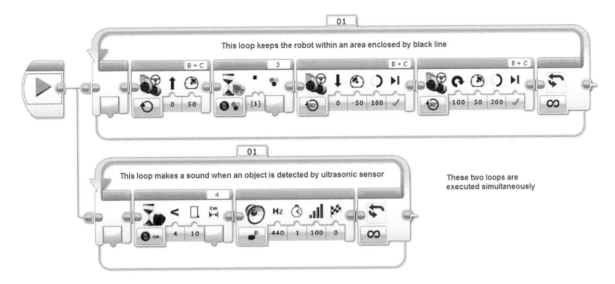

Wiring

> **NOTE**
>
> To create the parallel sequence, move your cursor near the start black (hover around). When the wire connection changes to blue, drag and connect the wires to the bottom loop. You can also use this wire connection to reduce the length of the long sequence of blocks.

Recreate this program, download, and run. Move your hands in front of the robot and see what happens.

Important points to remember while multitasking

Make sure you are not using conflicting statements. For example, in one of the tasks, motors may be programmed to go forward, and in another parallel task, motors may be programmed to go backward. In such cases, your robot's behavior will be unpredictable.

Multitasking is extremely useful to create an emergency stop. You can use the Loop Interrupt Block under certain conditions (such as touch sensor activation) and stop the robot from creating any damage.

Instead of using the wires to connect, you can also multitask with more than one start block. In the example below, a third motor is used. If you got this far, you can build your own robot with an additional motor.

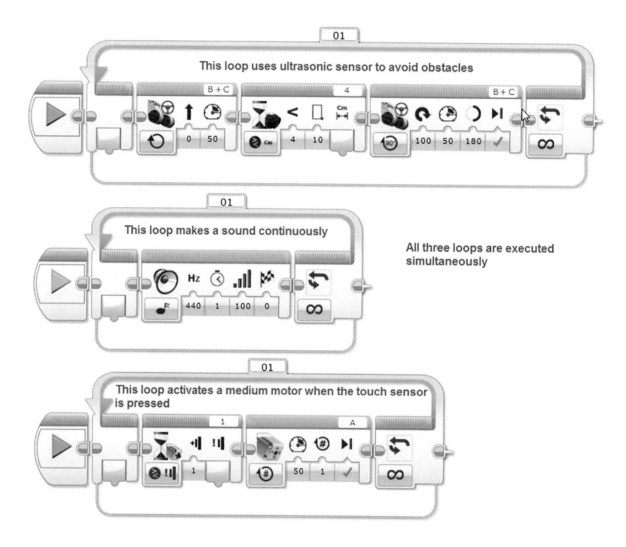

All three loops are executed simultaneously

Mission 20: Multitasking with a touch sensor

Create a multitasking program that makes your robot roam around inside a circle while the third motor constantly swings back and forth about 30° when the touch sensor is pressed.

15

Conditional Branching—Switch

We make decisions every day, sometimes without realizing we do. For instance, if we see a red traffic light while driving, we stop. If we are hungry at home, we open the fridge and look for something to eat. Sometimes we have options. For example, instead of eating at home, we can go outside.

An important decision-making statement is: If something happens or is true, do this, or else do that. This is a *conditional branching statement*. Every programming language has conditional statements. We have a Switch Programming Block, which is a Flow block, that can help us to implement conditional branching statements. For example, we may want our robot top keep going until something is in its way. If any object is too close to our robot, we want the robot to stop, flash a red light, and make a sound.

STUDENT LEARNING OUTCOMES

- To formulate a conditional branching statement switch with a programming block.

- To demonstrate how appropriate decisions can be made using a condition statement.

Switch Programming Block (Switch Block)

To understand how a Switch Block works, let us drag-and-drop a Switch Block, which can be found in the Data blocks category, into our programming area. Refer to the figure below. A Switch Block has two (top and bottom) areas. If a specified condition is true, what is on the top is executed. If the condition is not true, what is on the bottom is executed. By default, the Switch Block shows the touch sensor and two areas, upper and lower.

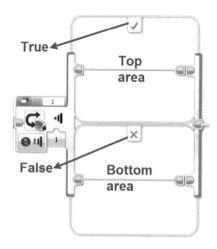

NOTE

There are more possible cases (not just two) with Switch Block. We will discuss that in the next example.

Now change the touch sensor to ultrasonic sensor. We want our robot to stop, flash a red light, and make a sound if it sees an object within 15 cm (150 mm). We can put that condition on the top area and leave the bottom area blank, as we do not need to do anything if no object is too close. The new Switch Block will look as shown at right.

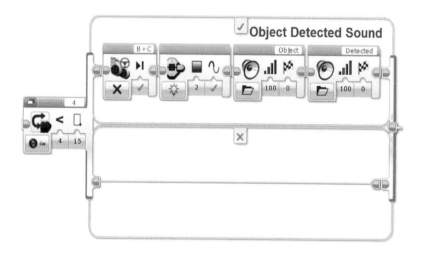

> **NOTE**
>
> On the top area, the Mover Steering Block is off, the brick status is 'LEDs Flashing,' and two Sound Blocks state 'Object Detected.' If nothing is in the way, the Switch Block will go to the bottom area and proceed further.

Programming Logic

The logic for this code can be written as:

- My robot keeps going.
- While on the way, if it sees an object, it will flash a light and make a sound.
- If not, it will keep going.

The complete program is shown below. Notice that everything is inside an infinite loop.

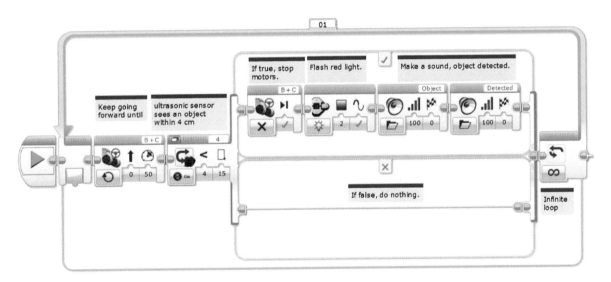

Students must learn to use the Switch Block properly. Let your students practice it with various options.

Mission 21: Touch sensor and the third motor

Write a program that will spin your medium motor (connected to Port A) when the touch sensor is pressed. Must be changed to "If not, display on the screen "Not Pressed."

Sample program for Mission 21

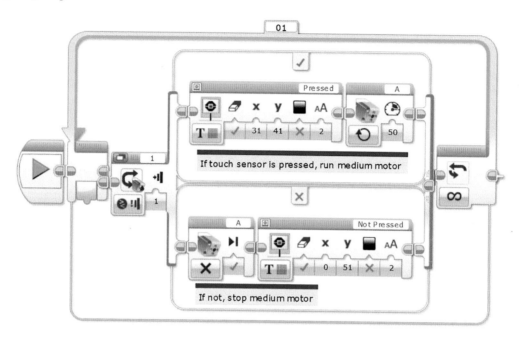

NOTE

You must switch off your medium motor if not pressed; otherwise, it will keep running.

Understanding Switch with Multiple Cases

In this case, our logic is simple, with only two choices:

1. If the object is closer than 150 mm, do this.

2. If not, do something else.

In real life, choices are neither this easy or binary. There may be other options. For example, a color is not always black and white. With our sensor we can measure as many as seven colors. How can we use the Switch Block to do this? This is discussed in the following example.

Color Recognition with Switch

Drag-and-drop a Switch Block and change the mode from default touch sensor to color sensor. We have two options: (1) to measure, or (2) to compare. We will choose the 'Measure' option to identify various colors. This is shown in the figure below left.

Color Sensor → Measure → Color Option

> **NOTE**
>
> The "+" sign enables you to add more cases, as shown in the figure below right. This option will appear only when available. (If you recall, this option was not available when we used the touch sensor.)

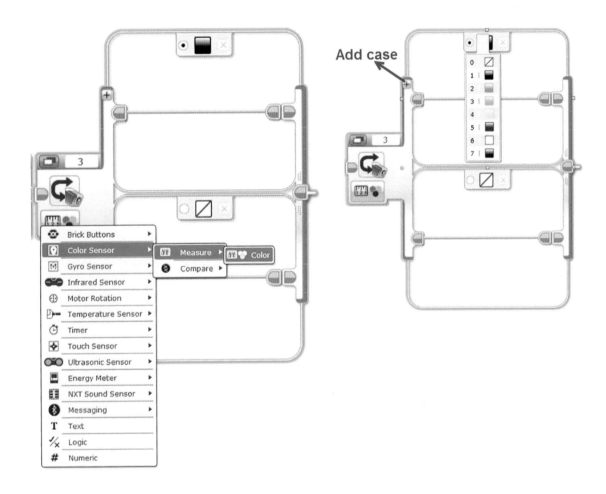

Mission 22: Multiple Color Identification

Write a program that will identify all seven possible colors using the color sensor. Make sure the program makes a distinct sound for each color. Put the switch inside a loop so we can keep checking various colors. Otherwise, your program will run only once. Put a colored paper under the light sensor and see if your program works.

Sample program for Mission 22

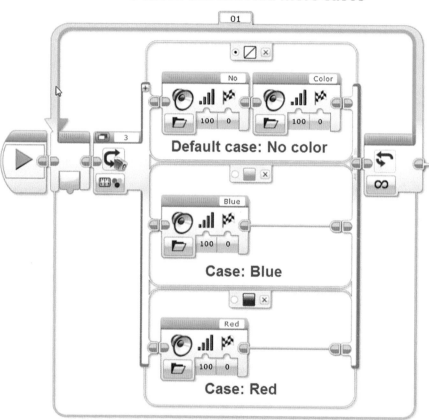

NOTE

Make sure you also have a case for 'No Color,' and make that the default case; it means our sensor cannot identify a particular color.

Mission 23: Color identification and display

Sound is fun but you can't hear it in noisy classroom or at Robot Rally. Create a program to identify colors and display the color on the LCD screen for 3 seconds.

> **NOTE**
>
> Same as the previous mission's program; just add a Display Block and specify the appropriate color.

16

Line-Following – Wiggler Approach

Line following is an important activity, and one of the most common applications in the real world. Robots use it in operations in warehouses and assembly lines. Line following is also fun and exciting. Line following events are conducted worldwide, and we want to make sure our students can take part in this activity.

STUDENT LEARNING OUTCOMES

- To write a program so their robot can follow a line using one color sensor;
- To explain 'Wiggler' motion.

Basic Line-Following Program using the Wiggler Approach

Line following requires a color sensor, which can be used in color sensor mode, allowing it to identify each color, or in reflected light mode. Both modes will work, and we must encourage our students to explore both options.

Reflected Light Intensity (RLI)

We will use the RLI for this program. Student must first measure the RLI value for the line—typically black—and the background—typically white or a bright color. Students must take several readings, find the average value for each, and record their readings in their notebook.

Programming Logic

The robot can start on the left or right side of the black line, or in the middle of the black line. Let us consider starting the robot when its color sensor is on the left, outside the black line (scenario A). This will lead the left edge following.

1. When the color sensor sees white, the robot must make a small turn to the right until it sees the black line.

2. When the color sensor sees black, the robot will make a small turn to the left until it sees the white line.

This process repeats forever, and the robot slowly wiggles forward. Scenario B shows right edge following. Scenario C shows starting on the black line with the option to follow left or right edge.

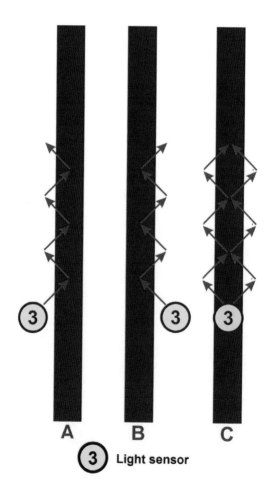

A   B   C

3 **Light sensor**

The first line-following program is always exciting. The Wiggler Approach is fun to watch. But keep in mind that this is not the way we follow lines; we normally won't wiggle when we do so. Inefficient as this approach is, it is easy to teach and implement. There are more advanced options students can explore on their own. We will discuss a few other methods in this guide as well.

This program will work well on both straight and curved lines with large radii. It may lose its track if the turns are too tight. You can reduce the power to make it follow the lines smoothly and negotiate tighter curves.

A note about turning: Students already know how to use Move Steering or Move Tank blocks for making turns. We will use the Move Tank Block for line-following, which gives more flexibility. Students may like to experiment with the Move Steering Block or use individual large motor blocks.

Sample Line-Following Program using the Wiggler Approach

In this program, I start my robot on the left side of the black line, so it will make a right turn first, and then a left turn. I am using RLI for this program, and my threshold value is 40. I used 50 for power, which gave good results. (When I made it faster, the robot had a problem at one of the turns.) Also notice that I am using the Move Tank Block, and one of the motors is always turned off.

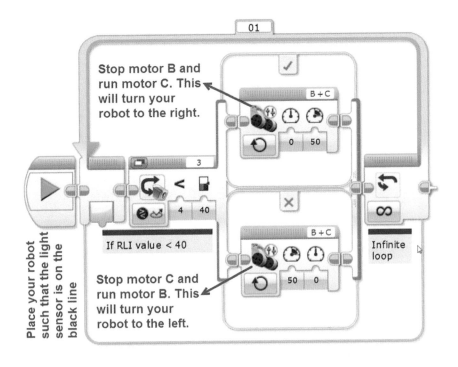

> **NOTE**
>
> Some students may like to use the color sensor mode instead of RLI. Let them explore that option. The program will remain the same, except that they have to choose the colors instead of using RLI.

Mission 24: Line-Following Challenge

Conduct a line-following challenge in your classroom. Make a simple course. You can do so with a black tape on a bright surface, or, if you have a large table with a dark surface, then you can apply a white tape onto it to create a course. As long the color sensor can distinctly differentiate between the two colors, any surface will work.

The robot will be given two chances to perform. You must use a stopwatch to measure the time. Ask students to note down the time it took for the robot to complete the course. A sample line-following course is below.

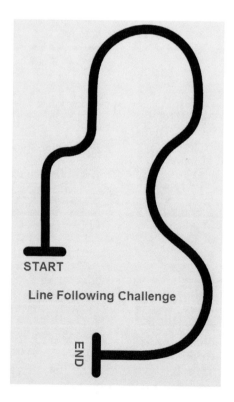

START

Line Following Challenge

END

17

Improved Line-Following

Instead of stopping a motor, we can increase its speed slightly. Experiment with various values. This will give the robot a smoother and faster line-following. This approach can significantly increase the robot's speed as much as 50%, if the line does not have sharp curves. Notice the value 25 for speed (instead of 'Off') in the following program. Students must vary this number and see how much they can improve the program through trial and error. The logic for this program is essentially the same as that of the previous unit, except that, instead of stopping one motor while turning, students are now allowed to move that motor, making the robot go faster.

STUDENT LEARNING OUTCOMES

- To improve their line-following more efficiently by eliminating all motor stops in the program.

Sample Improved Line-Following Program

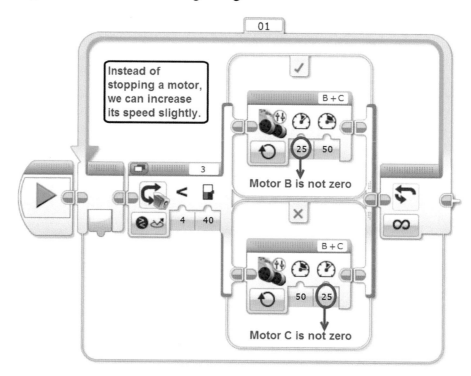

Mission 25: Improved Line-Following Challenge

Students are given two attempts to complete the same course using their new program. Use a table like the one below to record the data in your notebook. Compare the performance between two programs.

Approach	Attempt	Time (sec)	Comments
Basic Line-Following (Wiggler)	1		
	2		
	Best time		
Improved Line-Following	1		
	2		
	Best time		

18

Line-Following with Two Sensors

Most line-following events will allow the use of multiple sensors. Using two sensors can significantly improve the speed. All our students should know how to write and execute a line-following program using one light sensor. This is an optional activity.

STUDENT LEARNING OUTCOMES

- To devise a way to mount two color sensors;
- To write an efficient line-following program using three approaches.

Strategy For using two light sensors, students must devise a way to attach two color sensors facing down just outside the line. One line-following strategy using two color sensors is shown in the figure below. Notice that 2 and 3 are light sensors just outside the line to be followed (Scenario A). Motor B and C are also shown. When both sensors see white, the robot goes forward, because the black line is right in-between them. If the left sensor sees black (Scenario B), the robot must turn left. If the right sensor sees black (Scenario B), the robot must turn right.

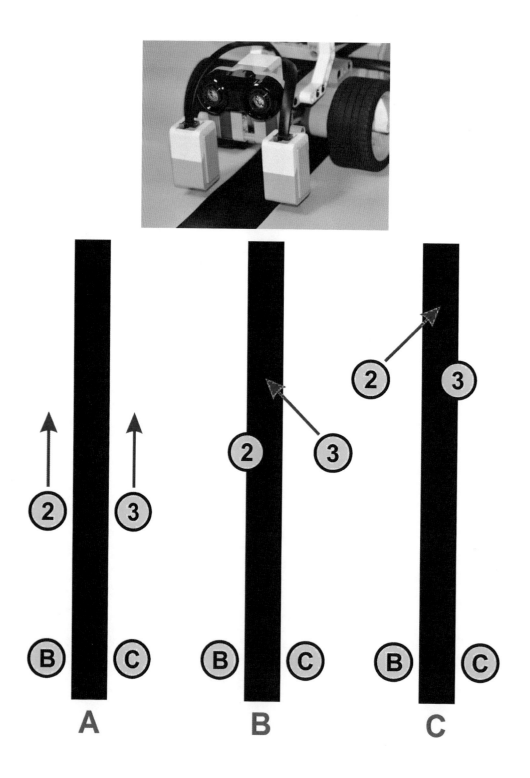

Sample program using two light sensors: Parallel Programming

> **NOTE**
>
> Instead of using a Move Tank Block, I am using a Large Motor Block to make the program look simpler.

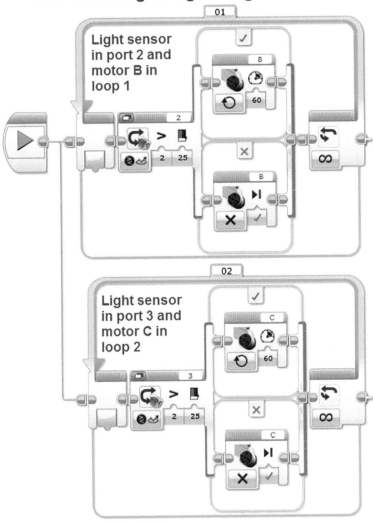

Line following using two light sensors

Sample program using two light sensors: 3 Switch Blocks

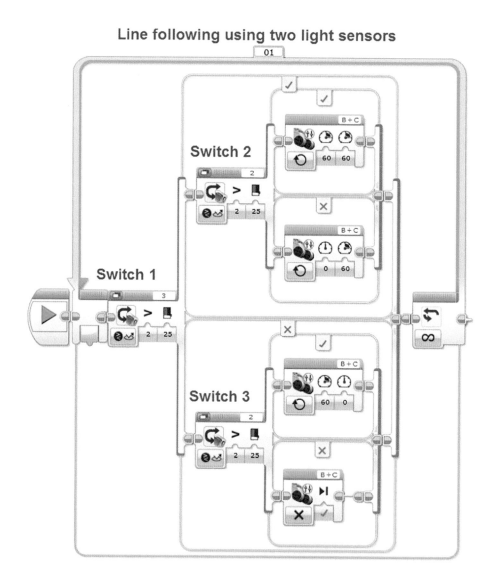

Line following using two light sensors

Mission 26: Fast Line-Following with Two Sensors

Students are given two attempts to complete the same course using their new program. Use a table like the one below to record the data in the notebook. Compare the performances among three programs.

Approach	Attempt	Time (sec)	Comments
Basic Line-Following (Wiggler)	1		
	2		
	Best time		
Improved Line-Following	1		
	2		
	Best time		
Line following using two light sensors – Method 1	1		
	2		
	Best time		
Line following using two light sensors – Method 2	1		
	2		
	Best time		

Common Mistakes

For each light sensor, make measurements for the threshold value separately. Do not assume that the measurement taken from one sensors is valid for the other.

Connect the motor and light sensors to appropriate ports. If you want to choose different ports, that is fine, but make sure those changes are reflected on your programs.

Mission 27: Use of Three Light Sensors (optional)

Can you use three light sensors? Will using three light sensors make any difference? Can you write a working program using three light sensors?

19

Sumo Robotics

In sumo robotics, two autonomous robots try to push each other out of a circular ring. The first robot to fall from the table loses, and the remaining robot advances to the next round. While pushing your opponent out of the ring is the most common way to win a bout, disabling your opponent (flipping, lifting, etc.) is strongly encouraged. The object is to push your opponent out of the ring, *not* to destroy the robot parts. A sumo robot must be designed to have fast reflexes, brute strength, and the ability to seek out an opponent.

A sumo robotics event brings together all of the skills learned over several weeks, as a culminating event. Invite students from other classes (who would do robotics next year) and their parents. This is a great activity to have during an open house.

STUDENT LEARNING OUTCOMES

- To build a new robot on their own for a sumo event;
- To program their robot for a sumo challenge;
- To write a simple program using just the color sensor;
- To use ultrasonic and touch sensors to improve the performance of the robot.

Passive Approach

A simple stay-inside-a ring-program you conducted earlier can be a sumo program. As your robot keeps wandering inside the ring, sooner or later it will encounter the other robot in the ring. Eventually, they will push each other, and a winner can be identified. Yet this is a passive approach, as the robot does not actively seek the opponent; their encounter is purely based on chance.

Active Approach

The robot slowly spins until it finds an opponent within a specified distance. (This is done using the ultrasonic sensor.) Once the robot sees an opponent, it charges toward it at full speed until it sees a black line. (This is done using the color sensor.) Upon seeing the black line, the robot retreats. This cycle repeats until one robot pushes the other robot outside the ring or time runs out. See the sample program below.

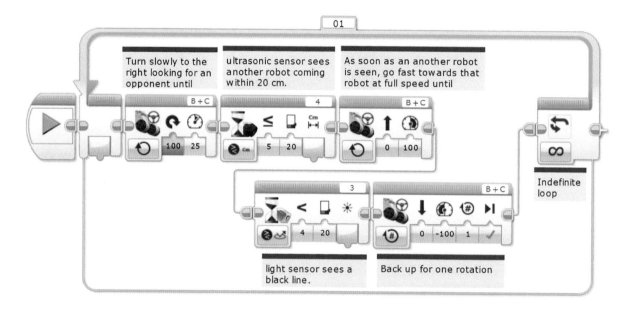

A sumo robotics event will take place in a circular ring nearly 4 feet in diameter with a one-inch white border along the ring's perimeter. The surface of the ring is smooth plywood (painted black) and is raised above ground level to help the judges determine when a robot has "fallen off."

A robot may fall apart during the event, so students must take the time to build a robot with a strong base. They are expected to use at least two sensors, but encourage them to use three sensors and three motors. The third motor can be used to hammer, push and/or lift the opponent's robot.

- Check the location of your robot's center of gravity.
- Is your robot too tall? Tall robots can easily flip.
- Can you increase the resistance when your robot is pushed?

Mission 28: Sumo Challenge – Rules

1. Your robot must be *autonomous*; once you hit the "Start" button, the robot is on its own to find its opponent and push it out of the ring. No human intervention is allowed once a bout starts.

2. At the start of each bout, the robots are placed inside the ring border, as indicated by the judge.

3. When both contestants are ready, the judge will signal the start of the bout, and the robots must be activated. Players must clear the Ring Area once the robots have been activated.

4. The robots will proceed in combat until one is disabled or removed from the ring. If robots are still in the ring at the end of the specified time (determined by judges on the day of the challenge based on the number of teams and other considerations), the bout is stopped, and either a winner or a rematch is announced.

5. If robots are stuck in an entanglement or deadlock, then the clock will be stopped and the bout restarted with both robots blindfolded (light sensors will be closed with a tape).

6. Judgment of the ring official is final.

7. Happy wrestling!

Links to earlier Sumo Robotics events at Cal Poly

Los Angeles Times **video:** http://www.youtube.com/watch?v=m3e25HMpPNI

Inland Valley Daily Bulletin: https://www.youtube.com/watch?v=n1n3eD5GZx8

20

Impromptu Obstacle Course

An obstacle course is perhaps the most difficult of all tasks. It requires hard work, patience, imagination and creativity. Since the course is not known in advance, students have very limited time to work out a course.

Students are required to program their robots to navigate through various obstacles, to go over a bump, to stop at a specified location for a specified time, and to identify the color at a specified zone and display that information on the LCD screen. There will be bonus points and penalties.

STUDENT LEARNING OUTCOMES

- To develop and implement a strategy to navigate the obstacle course;
- To take all necessary measurement from the obstacle course and transfer that information into a sketch in their notebook;
- To program their robot for an obstacle course challenge.

A sample obstacle course

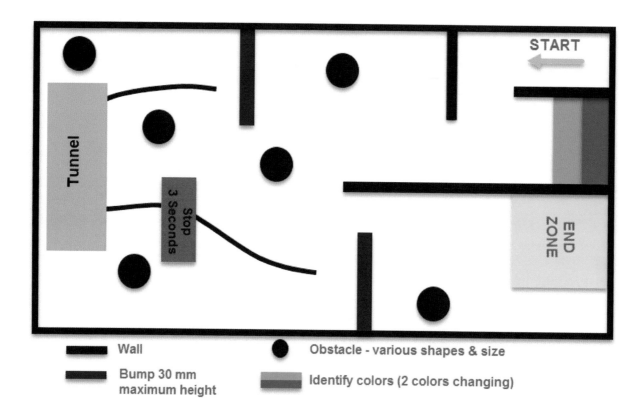

▬▬	Wall	⬤	Obstacle - various shapes & size
▬▬	Bump 30 mm maximum height	▬▬	Identify colors (2 colors changing)

21

Sensor Blocks

Our students have done a lot of work in the preceding weeks and learned much about building and programming robots. At times they had questions on how we could do things better. Many things can be done better with more advanced programming blocks. This section will cover some of these capabilities.

STUDENT LEARNING OUTCOMES

- To use various Sensor Blocks in their programming;
- To use data wires to transmit information from one block to another.

Description

Sensor Blocks, shown here in distinct yellow color, differ greatly from Wait Blocks, in that they receive data from the sensor and let you use that data with other programming blocks. For example, you can measure the distance with the ultrasonic sensor and use this information to control the power of your motors. Data Wire carries information (data) from one block to another block. For example, you can take an output from a Sensor Block and pass it on to another programming block.

Measure and Display

Our first task is to use ultrasonic Sensor Block to measure the distance from the sensor to an object and display on the screen. To do this, we need a Sensor Block and a Display Block. Makes sure you select Text mode (Pixel or Grid).

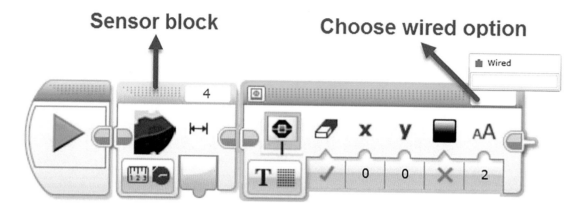

Once we select the wired option, the Display Block will show you a port where we can connect the data wire.

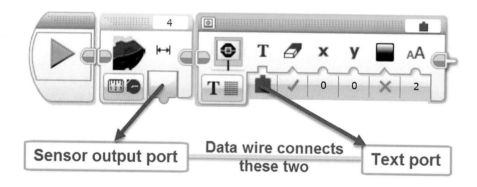

To create a data wire, hover over the sensor port until you see the wire connection change to blue. Click, hold and drag to the next port. Your data wire will connect the two ports neatly. These two blocks are put inside the loop to get a continuous reading. Run the program and look at the LCD screen. See how it changes. Move your hand in front of the sensor and what happens.

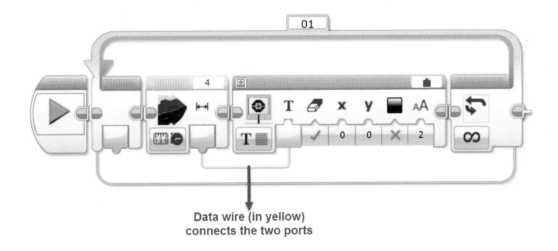

Data wire (in yellow)
connects the two ports

Mission 29: Go faster and faster if it becomes brighter and brighter

Let's say we want our robot to go faster when it becomes brighter. This means it will go faster if we place it on a white surface. Let your students do that on their own. Ask them to display the number on the LCD screen as the robot moves.

Programming Logic

Use a color Sensor Block (for sensing light) and a Move Steering Block to motion. Use the RLI option to get a reading between 0 and 100.

To make the movement continuous, we will put these two blocks inside a loop. Connect the sensor output to the motor power port. Add a Display Block and connect the sensor output

Sample program for Mission 29

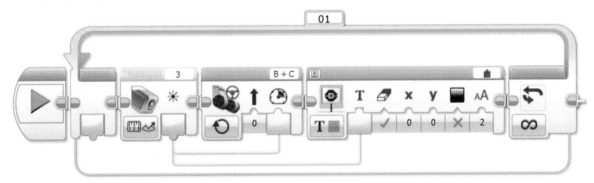

Mission 30: Find the Slope Angle

Slope is an important concept. We deal with slope whenever we go uphill or downhill. Slope is zero on a flat surface. Slope can be defined by angle. Just watch your parents drive the car: they will give it more gas when they go uphill, because they need more power to do so, because, the steeper the hill is, the harder it is for the car to go up.

The concept of slope is also very important in Algebra and Calculus. Depending upon the mathematical level of your students, you can give them slope experiments to perform. You can ask them to measure the rise and run, calculate the slope, and compare the results. This is also an opportunity to introduce trigonometry to them.

We want our robot to go on the slope and tell us the angle of the ramp. So we need to set up a simple ramp, as shown in the figure below. You can use a piece of wood to create the ramp. Just make sure your robot can transition from the floor to the ramp without getting stuck. You may have to put something to smooth out the transition.

Ask students to use the Gyro Block to figure out the slope angle and display it on the screen. To measure this angle, the gyro sensor must be mounted properly on the robot so that the gyro's face is vertical to the axis of rotation (shown in the figure below).

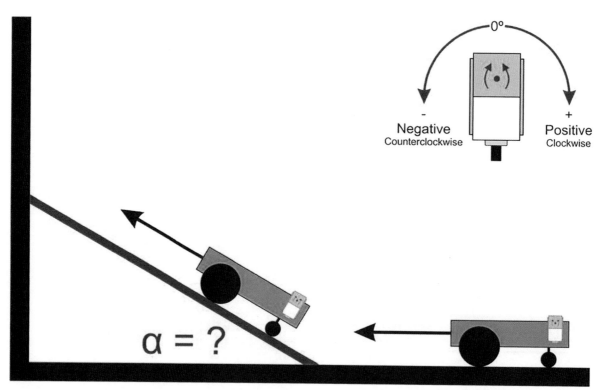

Programming Logic

- Reset the gyro block. The reset automatically sets the angle of the sensor to zero.

- Use a Move Steering Block to keep the robot moving for a certain amount of rotations until it is fully on the ramp.

- Display the gyro output on the Display Block. Wait a few seconds for the display to appear.

Sample program for Mission 30

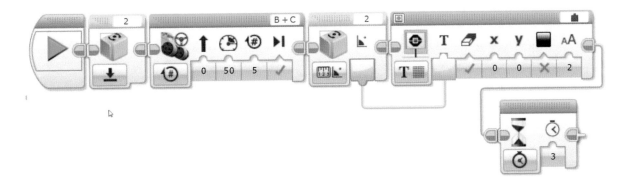

22

Data Operations

We have used Action Blocks, Flow Blocks and Sensor Blocks so far. Data Blocks let us read and write variables, compare values, perform math operations, and much more. They are easy to use, and, in conjunction with other blocks, we can do some very advanced programming with our robot.

STUDENT LEARNING OUTCOMES

- To use various Data Blocks, including the Math and Variable/Constant blocks;
- To perform basic math operations to calculate averages, circle areas, and angle degrees on a triangle.

Math Block: Calculating the average (arithmetic mean)

To get started, let us perform some simple math operations to become familiar with Data Blocks.

Let us add two numbers and find the average. To do so, drag-and-drop a Math Block from data operations into our programming area.

Note: In the figure at right, the Math Block shows many options that include basic arithmetic operations. The letters 'a' and 'b' are the values we need to supply. For now, we will type in those values, but usually they will be passed on from some calculations.

So we will type in two values, say, 60 and 75. We can change these values at any time. We will have to add them and then divide by 2. We then want to display the number on the screen.

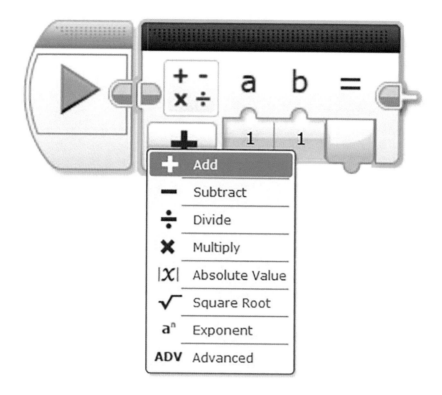

Below is the sample program. Notice the use of data wires and the Wait Block at the end of Display Block, so you can read the result of the operation.

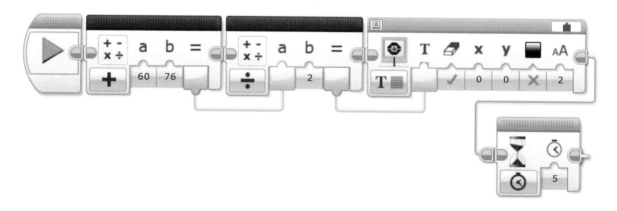

You can change the values and run the program to get the new result. This is a very simple operation, and yet it does show what you can do with EV3.

Mission 31: Calculate the average of 4 numbers and display the result

This can be done in different ways. The easiest way to do this is to use the Math Block ADV option, which allows us to manipulate four numbers. Students will probably use four Math Blocks (three to add, one to divide). Both possibilities are shown in the figure below.

Example: 75, 92, 46, 151

Determining the average of four numbers using using four math

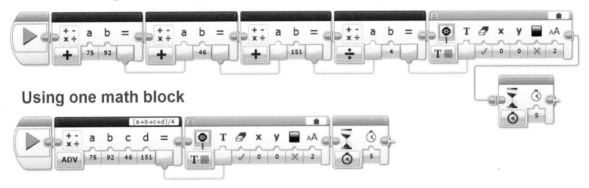

Using one math block

Mission 32: Calculate the area of a circle

The formula for the area of a circle is:

$$A = \pi r^2$$

In this formula, is a constant and is approximately equal to 3.14. To write this program, we will use:

- a Constant Block to store 3.14;
- a Variable Block to assign the value of the radius, which we can change when necessary;
- a Math Block to multiply;
- a Display Block to show the result;
- a Wait Block to hold the result.

> **NOTE**
>
> To use a Variable Block, give the variable a name, and then write the value you want to store into the block. You can then access the value by reading.

Sample program for Mission 32

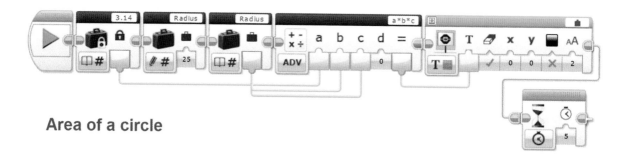

Area of a circle

Mission 33: Calculate the area of a triangle

The formula for the area of a triangle is:

$$A = \frac{1}{2} bh$$

Sample program for Mission 33

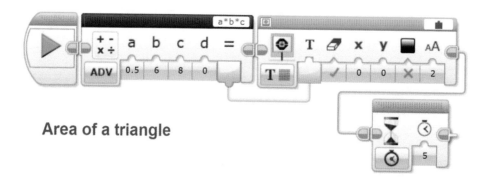

Area of a triangle

Mission 34: Calculate the area of a square

Write a program to make your robot trace a square that is 2 rotations long on each side. Your robot must complete the square and display the area at the end.

Mission 35: Random Dance

Write a program that will create a dance motion for your robot. Use a Random Number Block.

23

Advanced Programming

Be it sumo robotics or line-following, students must make measurements to input the reflect light values. This is important when you travel to other locations and use different tables and mats, as these values change from place to place.

However, students may not always have a computer handy to download the program with new values. Even if they borrow someone else's computer, that program may not be on it. It is much easier if their program can sense the new lighting conditions and adjust automatically.

This is what we will do in this unit. We will do a line-following program, for which we will make measurements interactively without reprogramming the robot.

STUDENT LEARNING OUTCOMES

- To utilize Sensor Blocks to collect data, perform calculations using Data Blocks, and control the robot;

- To write programs that will automate measurements for lien following program without reprogramming;

- To write advanced programs using proportional control .

Line-Following

We need readings from black and white lines for line-following. We normally use the robot to measure these readings and then use them in the program. Let us assume we will use the basic wiggler algorithm for simplicity. The program is reproduced in the figure below for convenience.

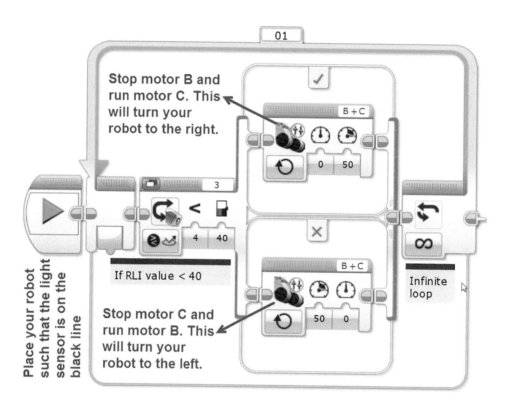

Stop motor B and run motor C. This will turn your robot to the right.

If RLI value < 40

Stop motor C and run motor B. This will turn your robot to the left.

Infinite loop

Place your robot such that the light sensor is on the black line

In this code, we are using 40 as RLI value. Instead of typing in this value, we want to make measurements at the location where our line-following program runs. The complete program is shown in the figure below.

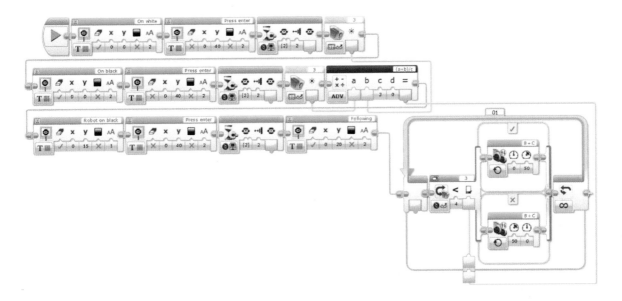

Programming Logic Explanation

- In the first step, a message is displayed to place the robot on the white background.
- The Wait Block with brick button waits for your input.
- When you press 'Enter,' the Sensor Block collects RLI value and sends it to the Math Block.
- Next, a message is displayed to place the robot on the black line.
- The Wait Block with brick button waits for your input.
- When you press 'Enter,' the Sensor Block collects RLI value and sends it to the Math Block.
- The Math Block adds these two values, divides by two, and sends the resulting number to the Switch Block, where the threshold value is required.
- A message is displayed to place the robot at the proper location.
- The Wait Block with brick button waits for your input.
- The robot starts to follow the line.

Mission 36: Advanced line-following with Interactive RLI measurement

Ask students to write an advanced line-following program with RLI values collated interactively.

Mission 37: Cave Explorer

We use robots for exploration. We have landed robots on other planets. Robots can be used anywhere where safety is an issue for humans. In this assignment we want you to design and program a robot for cave exploration. Since we do not know the cave's depth, before we go in we want our robot to go inside as deeply as possible, figure out the color of the cave floor, and come back and tell us how far it went (distance in meters), as well as the floor color.

> **NOTE**
>
> Make sure the rotation sensor (shown at right) displays how many degrees (or rotations the robot made) and uses that number for figuring out the distance.

Also, it is good practice to reset the rotation sensor before your robot starts.

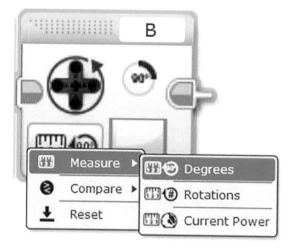

Sample Cave Explorer Program

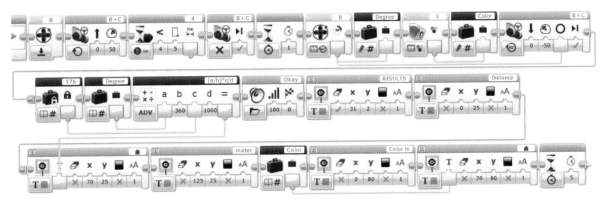

Cave Explorer Program Explanation

- Our cave explorer makes the trip. It goes as far as possible straight until the ultrasonic sensor sees something within 5 cm, and it stops.

- The rotation sensor measures and sends the total degree traveled to the Math Block and the Move Steering Block.

- The robot backs up the same distance it traveled forward.

- Math Block divides the total degree measurement by 360 and then multiplies the value by the wheel circumference, which is already stored in the Math Block as 176 mm. This value is then divided by 1,000 to convert it into meters. This data is sent to a Display Block.

- Meanwhile, the Color Sensor Block measures the color and sends the color code (0 to 7) to another Display Block. (There are several Display Blocks to give the results in an easy-to-read format.)

Mission 38: Smooth Line-Following

You probably noticed that our robot does not follow a line or a wall smoothly, often deviating from the path we want it to take. Despite our efforts, this happens, and it can be frustrating. Here is a simple yet effective program that adjusts the steering based on the difference between the light-sensor reading and the maximum (or minimum) RLI value, which is multiplied to fine-tune and control the two motors individually.

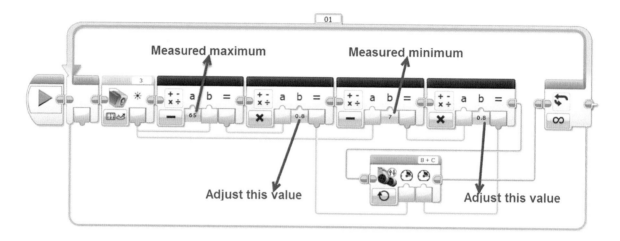

Mission 39: Proportional Control

For line-following, we have been using two-state control (on-off) for our robot, with no feedback to correct it. Engineers spend a lot of time studying control systems; a proportional control system is one step beyond on-off. PID controllers use basic types: P – proportional, I – integrative, and D – derivative.

We will focus on developing a proportional control program for smoothly following a line. We will correlate the change in light readings to steering control. The basic idea behind proportional control is to calculate the error (or deviation) from our desired value and to apply a correction.

Programming Logic

- In this program, we have chosen a value of 25% for motor power.
- We have also introduced a gain factor with a value of 100. We can change this value later when we fine-tune our robot.
- We have also measured the maximum and minimum light reading from our line and the background. These values happen to be 100 (for white) and 14 (for our gray mat background). I highly recommend automating the measurement of these values instead of typing them in.

- Range is calculated by subtracting minimum for maximum. We will use this value to normalize the error later.

- Target value is the average of maximum and minimum.

- Once the program starts, we get a light reading and subtract it from the average. This is the calculated error, which can be positive or negative.

- We multiply the error by the gain. This is done to increase the response to the error. This factor 100 can be changed.

- We divide the value from the above step by the range. This is the adjusted correction value. In general, you will not see people dividing by the range explicitly. By dividing the error (which is reflected light) by the range (which is also light), we are normalizing the error. Other programs implicitly divide the gain (100, in our case) by range (100, in theory). This will give 1 as the value for the ideal proportional constant.

- The final step is to take this adjusted value and add or subtract the motor power. We are using two motors, so we will use the Move Tank Block. Depending upon the position of your robot (left side or right side following), you will have to wire these as input to appropriate motors.

$$Power\ (Motor\ B) = MPower\ + \frac{Gain}{Range} \times (RLI\ reading - Target\ Value)$$

$$Power\ (Motor\ C) = MPower\ - \frac{Gain}{Range} \times (RLI\ reading - Target\ Value)$$

- Run the program and see how your robot behaves. Adjust the values for MPower and Gain until you achieve the desired results.

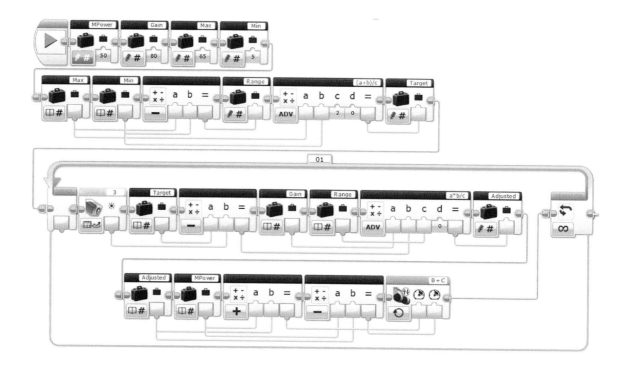

Mission 40: Touch Count

Touch sensor is a very useful tool for many applications. Its most popular application is for checking whether the robot comes in contact with another object. Touch sensor can also be used like a counter. For example, we may want to see how many times the robot hits a ball or knocks at a door. In these cases, we want to count the number of times a button is pressed and display that number on the screen.

Write a program to count the number of times touch sensor is bumped (pressed and released).

Sample program for Mission 40

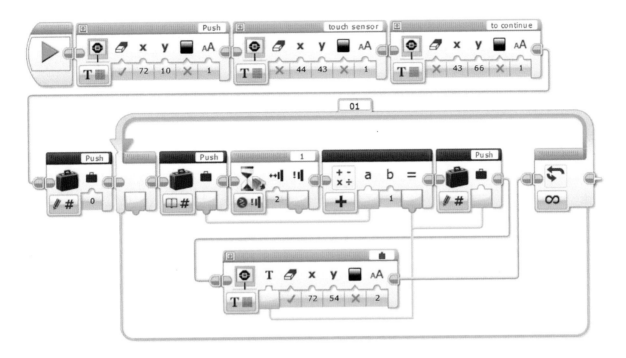

Mission 41: Fibonacci sequence

A Fibonacci sequence is a series of numbers. The sequence starts with 0 and 1, and each subsequent number is the sum of the previous two numbers. So the sequence is:

$$0, 1, 1, 2, 3, 5, 8, 13, 21, 34, 55, 89, 144, \text{etc.}$$

The Fibonacci sequence is named after the Italian mathematician Leonardo of Pisa, a.k.a. Fibonacci, who wrote about this sequence in 1202 in his book *Liber Abaci*. The sequence is encountered in nature and related to the Golden Ratio, in that the ratio of two successive Fibonacci numbers leads to a Golden Ratio, which occurs in a pair of quantities with a ratio that is the same as the ratio of their sum to the larger of the two quantities (e.g., $a + b$ is to a as a is to b).

We can use the EV3 brick, not only to command your robot to perform various tasks, but also to write codes and perform mathematical operations as your personal computer does, and to display the results on the screen.

For your robot's mission, write a program to calculate and display the Fibonacci numbers.

Sample program for Mission 41

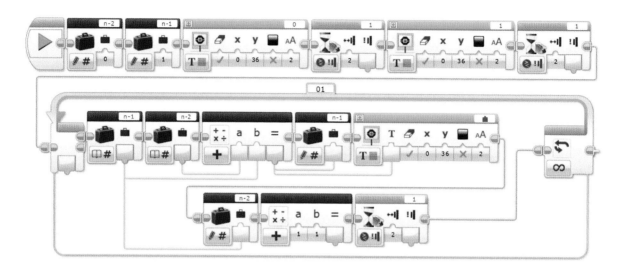

Mission 42: Multiplication Table

Write a program to display the multiplication table 12.

Sample program for Mission 42

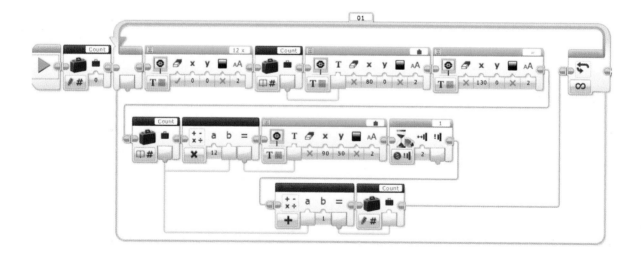

Appendix A

Glossary of Terms

Algorithm: A strategy that lays out a clear, step-by-step procedure to solve a problem.

Axle: A slender member with the primary function to transmit rotation motion. Strictly speaking, LEGO® axles should be called 'shafts.'

Beam: A structural element with holes to connect to other members using pins. Beams come in various sizes and are identified by the number of holes. Non-straight beams include L-beams, bent beams, etc.

Bushings: In engineering applications, bushings support shafts. In LEGO® Robotics, bushings are mostly spacers. They come in two different sizes.

Coding: The use of codes in computer programming.

Color sensor: A device that differentiates colors. The LEGO® color sensor can distinguish six colors.

Debugging: A process for locating and remediating errors. To avoid problems, it is better to include comments in our code.

EV3 Brick: The third generation of the LEGO® Robotics controller (RCX and NXT), based on the ARM 9 processor with the Linux-based operating system. It has four input and four output ports.

Frequency: How many times something is repeated over a particular period of time. The unit for frequency is Hertz (Hz).

Gear: A toothed wheel transmitting rotation motion. Gears are identified by their number of teeth.

Graphical Programming: A programming language in which graphic icons are used to create the program, instead of text.

Gyroscopic sensor: A device that measures angular velocity. The LEGO® Gyro Sensor measures the robot's rotational motion and changes in its orientation.

Infrared Sensor (IR): A device that bounces infrared waves off objects to determine how far they are from the sensor. The robot kit we use does not come with an IR sensor; we use an ultrasonic sensor.

LED: Light Emitting Diode. It emits light when an electric current passes through it.

Line-Following: Programming your robot to follow a line of certain thickness, color and complexity (straight or curved; if curved, the smallest radius on the line) as fast as possible. There are numerous line-following algorithms. Many line-following programs use more than one sensor.

Loop: A concept used in every programming language. It is one of the basic logical structures. A loop keeps iterating a set of instructions until specified conditions are reached.

Motor: An actuating device that converts electrical energy to mechanical energy. LEGO® motors are called Servo Motors, and they use feedback from an internal tachometer for precise control. There are two large motors and one medium motor. You can add an extra motor.

Obstacle Avoidance: Programming your robot to navigate through a difficult terrain with many objects of various sizes and shapes obstructing the way without touching them. Rules vary according to the event, which can be indoor or outdoor. Real-world applications such as self-driving cars, autonomous robots and robots for exploring outer space will greatly benefit from this application.

Pi: The ratio of a circle's circumference to its diameter, denoted by the Greek letter π, normally numbered as 3.14.

Pins: Connectors used to link beams together.

Friction pins resist motion and should be used when making static structures.

Smooth pins allow rotation and should be used when designing mechanisms.

Double pins can be friction pins or smooth pins. Use them to connect three beams.

Axle pins can also be friction pins and smooth pins.

Point Turn: The rotation of two motors at equal and opposite speeds, which causes the robot to spin in place. For the same robot, the radius of rotation during a point turn is half that of a swing turn.

Programming language: A set of instructions, commands, rules, syntax and semantics for communicating with and controlling computers. Computer programming is the same as coding for all practical purposes.

Proportional Control (P): An algorithm used to control systems. In P-controller, the control efforts (output) are proportional to the error, which makes it proportional control. In our robotics, we use proportional control to program a robot to follow a line or wall smoothly.

Rim: A circular part onto which a tire is mounted.

Shaft: A slender rod designed to transmit torque. (We use the term 'axle' more frequently than 'shaft' in LEGO® Robotics.)

Slope: A measure of steepness. Slope can be defined by the slope angle or by the ratio of the vertical distance to the horizontal distance.

Sound: A wave that propagates through a medium such as air or water.

Sumo Robotics: An event in which two robots attempt to push each other out of a ring. The sumo table size, robot size and rules vary, depending upon the event.

Swing Turn: The rotation of two motors at different speeds. Often in swing turns, one motor is spinning while the other is stopped. For the same robot, the radius of rotation during a swing turn is twice that of a swing turn.

Switch: A conditional statement in programming languages that allows you to branch out based on various conditions. It is easier to visualize this concept using 'if, then' statements from everyday life.

Tire: A doughnut-shaped part that covers the rim.

Touch sensor: A device that detects the push and release.

Ultrasonic sensor: A device that generates high-frequency sound waves (that we can't hear) and measures the time for receiving the echo.

User Interface (UI): A software that allows us to connect and interact with the computer.

Wheel: A two-part circular assembly designed to support a robot and move it easily on the ground. A wheel is connected by an axle to the motor or gearbox.

Made in the USA
Columbia, SC
06 June 2018